Design of MACHINES

ROLLAND T. HINKLE

Professor of Mechanical Engineering
Michigan State University

PRENTICE-HALL, INC.

Englewood Cliffs, New Jersey
1957

Library of Congress Catalog Card Number: 57-11087

Printed in the United States of America
20087

Design of MACHINES

PREFACE

This book is primarily for use in a second course in machine design. Even though there is a considerable amount of reference material included here, it is desirable that the student keep his first course book to use with this one.

The sections on theory can be used as needed. While some of this has been covered in previous courses, it is felt that a review with a different viewpoint will help to fix the theory in mind.

In the long problems the degree of guidance varies. This was done so that the instructor can put the student on his own and force him to make his own decisions. If the instructor wishes, he can give additional guidance or select portions of the problems and assign them as short problems.

Material taken directly from other sources is acknowledged in the book. The author wishes to express appreciation to: Professors Ching-U Ip and I. E. Morse of Michigan State University for their help and encouragement during the writing of this book; Professor M. L. Price of Worcester Polytechnic Institute for permission to base the centrifugal coupling problem on his work; and Mr. R. W. Evans, chief engineer, Carrier Conveyor Corporation, for his cooperation in furnishing general information and design details that are associated with the conveyor problem. The author especially wishes to express gratitude to his former teacher and colleague, Professor Paul H. Black of Ohio University, who, through the years, has influenced the author's way of thinking about machine design.

Rolland T. Hinkle

CONTENTS

Chapter 10:

DEFLECTION OF NON-UNIFORM BEAM   125

Chapter 11:

MANUAL LIFT TRUCK   135

Appendix:

DESIGN DATA   141

Design of MACHINES

Chapter 1

INTRODUCTION

The design of machines comprises one of the broadest areas in engineering and differs from other areas in that much of it is not exact. This area is not exact because theory has not kept pace with the needs of the designer. In mechanical design there are more than the usual number of indeterminate quantities. Unlike the design of electronic equipment, very few machines can be designed by using only stock items of known characteristics. The following example[1] will illustrate a type of problem which the designer often encounters. "With the correct bearing sizes determined, the theoretical bending, compression and torsional stresses are computed for comparison with previous designs. These calculations fall short of accuracy because of the complex nature of the crankshaft structure. However, after a number of successful engines have been manufactured, the method serves as a basis for checking the new design."

Since there are few basically new machines, the practice of comparing a new design with the design of an existing machine that has proved satisfactory is very common. The designer, if he has used all available theory, should feel no need for apology when he compares a new design with that of an existing machine.

Two extreme types of design are: that of a machine for mass production, such as an automobile engine, and that of a machine of which only one is to be built, such as a large testing machine. The designs of these two extreme types, like the broad range of intermediate types (with a few exceptions such as military equipment, certain scientific equipment, and machines controlled by law for public safety) are dominated almost entirely by economics.

---

[1] W. W. Kaufman, "Design of Forged Crankshafts for Heavy Duty Engines," *Design News*, March 15, 1955.

Large sums of money are often spent on the design, development, and testing of a new automobile engine even though it appears to be only slightly different from an existing engine. It is not uncommon for such engines to develop trouble after the automobile has been put on the market, and the manufacturer, admitting design errors, replaces certain parts free of charge. The principal reason for this is that in order to meet competition, a manufacturer must rate his engine as high as possible, and he must design the engine close to its performance limit in order to save a cent or two on each part. In this type of design great reliance is put on testing, and sometimes this is not adequate.

A number of years ago an automobile company put a low-powered car on the market and instead of using the transmission for the higher-powered model, a smaller transmission was designed. One of the basic principles of design is to use as many standard parts as possible to reduce manufacturing costs and to facilitate repair in the field. However, in this case the production was large enough to make it more economical to design and build the smaller transmission. The problem was not considered in its broader aspects and one fact was overlooked. The drivers of the low-powered cars found it necessary to shift gears even on moderate hills and as a result of excessive shifting, the transmissions wore out before the rest of the car.

At the other extreme — the design of a single machine — the procedure is usually quite different from that of a mass-produced machine. Testing and development, as they are used in mass-produced machines, are avoided as much as possible, and the designer puts forth every effort to make his first design satisfactory. Success in the first attempt can often be achieved by using a factor of safety that is larger than that used in a mass-produced machine, and by using as many purchased components as possible, such as clutches, brakes, bearings, gear reducers, etc. It is usually cheaper to buy such items when they are not needed in large quantities. Another advantage is that they are of proven quality. In comparison with the mass-produced machine, the relative cost of designing a single machine is usually much greater, and the cost of materials is much less. A single machine that is designed with a factor of safety of 4 may cost only a small percentage more than one built with a factor of safety of 2. If the machine proves unsatisfactory and has to be rebuilt, the time consumed in rebuilding the machine may exceed the contract time. Such an increase in time may be very expensive, as there is often a penalty for exceeding the contract time, e.g., one hundred dollars a day for each day beyond the contract delivery date.

In the intermediate type of design, that is, design for limited production, a combination of the above procedures is used. A procedure for each new design must be laid out after all of the factors have been considered.

In the successful design, the theoretical and the practical must be combined. This will be illustrated with two examples. In an impact machine for testing steel strapping, difficulty was encountered in the design of a simple, compact clamp for holding the strap. The clamp would not hold when the surfaces were smooth, and knurling the surfaces weakened the strap. The solution shown in Fig. 1.1 was found to be satisfactory. The smooth surfaces of the

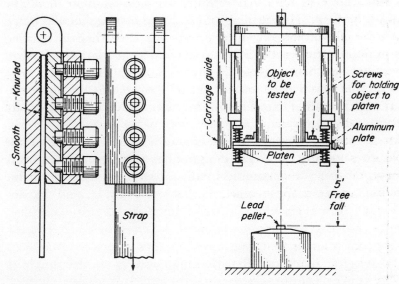

Fig. 1.1. Clamp for holding strap in testing machine.

Fig. 1.2. Impact testing machine.

clamp carried enough load to prevent the strap from breaking at the knurled surfaces.

In the design of an impact testing machine, Fig. 1.2, calculations showed that the stress in the platen was high even though it was massive and made of high strength steel. It was necessary to bolt the object to be tested to the platen, but drilling holes in the platen raised the induced stress above the endurance limit. A satisfactory solution was found by mounting a ½ inch thick aluminum alloy plate on top of the platen. Since the strength of the plate was not included in the calculations, it could be drilled and tapped at will. The platen was left undrilled except at the four corners where the carriage was spring-mounted.

In the two cases cited above, the solutions can be considered as practical, but they were reached only after the theory had been exhausted, and they did not violate theory. Theory did not lead directly to the correct solutions, but it eliminated unsatisfactory ones.

Another aspect of design that must be considered is that of quality. Sales, production, and design groups often have different ideas about the requirement of quality. One automobile manufacturer recently supplied its dealers with standard mufflers and also with rustproof ones that retailed for a dollar more than the standard mufflers. The dealers found that they were unable to sell the rustproof mufflers and in order to clear their shelves, reduced the price of the rustproof mufflers to that of the standard ones. Most of the customers believed that they would trade their cars before a third muffler was needed and would let the next owner replace it. Many people believe that the manufacturer should install rustproof mufflers at the factory and raise the price of the car fifty cents or a dollar to cover the cost, but the manufacturers believe that the public does not want this. The designer has the moral responsibility of incorporating the maximum quality that is possible within the price limit set by management.

Chapter 2

BASIC CONCEPTS

2.1. *Introduction*

The work that the reader has had in mechanics and strength of materials has probably been presented in small units of single concepts, and the problems that followed each small block of work pertained only to the previous concept. Problems that do not lend themselves to exact analysis are usually avoided. The avoidance of such problems is probably necessary in the presentation of new theories.

In the typical design problem the student must decide on the proper theory to use, he must often consider several theoretical aspects, and in some cases, because of complexities, the student cannot obtain an exact solution. The problem cannot always be easily identified with a particular section in a book. A study of machine design not only serves as a review of basic theory but helps to integrate it. The engineer is not expected to remember all of the work that he has had in school, but he is expected to remember the topics that he has had and be able to look them up, review them, and then apply them. However, the successful designer cannot work with a completely blank mind and depend on looking up everything that he needs. A certain amount of basic knowledge must be stored permanently in the mind and be so close to the surface that when a problem is approached, the pertinent basic concepts will automatically come into the consciousness. Numerical values and equations need not be remembered, because they can be looked up. In the remainder of this chapter some of the basic concepts will be discussed in detail. Although most of the concepts are not new to the reader, a review of them from a somewhat different viewpoint should help to fix these concepts in his mind and to make them more useful.

2.2. *Plane Equilibrium*

The following three expressions should always be in the designer's mind.

$$\Sigma F_v = 0 \tag{2.1}$$

$$\Sigma F_h = 0 \tag{2.2}$$

$$\Sigma M = 0 \tag{2.3}$$

In Fig. 2.1 it is known that $P_1 + P_2 = R_1 + R_2$ because expression (2.1) must be satisfied.

In a physical sense, a moment is the product of a force and the perpendicular distance from the force to the point about which the moment is acting, or, if more than one force is acting, the sum of the individual moments. In Fig. 2.1, expression (2.3) can be used to

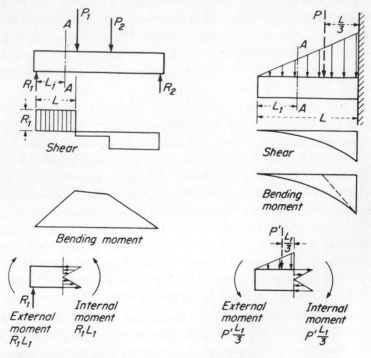

Fig. 2.1. Loaded beam, showing external and internal moments.

Fig. 2.2. Loaded beam, showing external and internal moments.

determine R_1 by summing the moments about R_2. The shear and bending moment diagrams are shown below the beam. The bending moment at load P_1 is R_1L, which is also the area of the shaded portion of the shear diagram since the height and length of the diagram are R_1 and L, respectively. This has led to the use of the shear diagram for determining moments, but it is somewhat artificial and many designers seldom use it. At section A-A, the bending moment, $R_1 L_1$, can be used for determining the stress in the beam at A-A, because at this section there is an internal resisting moment of equal magnitude but opposite sense.

The shear and bending moment diagrams for a cantilever with a non-uniformly distributed load are shown in Fig. 2.2. With this type of loading, the shear diagram is a curved line which sometimes makes it inconvenient to determine the included area. The moment at the support can be determined by replacing the distributed load with a force, P, equal in magnitude to the distributed load and acting through the centroid of the load diagram. The bending moment diagram for this load is shown as a dotted line. For any other section, A-A, the moment can be determined by using the load at the left of the section.

2.3. *Hooke's Law*

"Take then a quantity of even-drawn wire, either Steel, Iron, or Brass, and coyl it on an even cylinder into a Helix of what number of turns you please, then turn the ends of the wire into loops, by one of which suspend this coyl upon a nail and by the other restrain the weight that you would have to extend it [Fig. 2.3], and hanging on several weights observe exactly to what length its own weight doth extend it, and you shall find that if one ounce, or one pound, or one certain weight doth lengthen it one line or one inch or one certain length, then two ounces, or two pounds, or two weights will extend it two lines, two inches or two lengths and three ounces, pounds or weights, three lines, inches or lengths and so forwards."[1]

By a spring, Hooke did not mean the ordinary conventional spring; he meant any "springy" body whatsoever, and he attempted to define a "spring" by referring to a long list of materials which he considered to be of a "springy" nature.

Hooke's law is often stated in terms of stress being proportional to strain, or stress being proportional to load. However, in some

---

[1] H. F. Girvin, *A Historical Appraisal of Mechanics* (Scranton, Penna.: International Textbook Co., 1948).

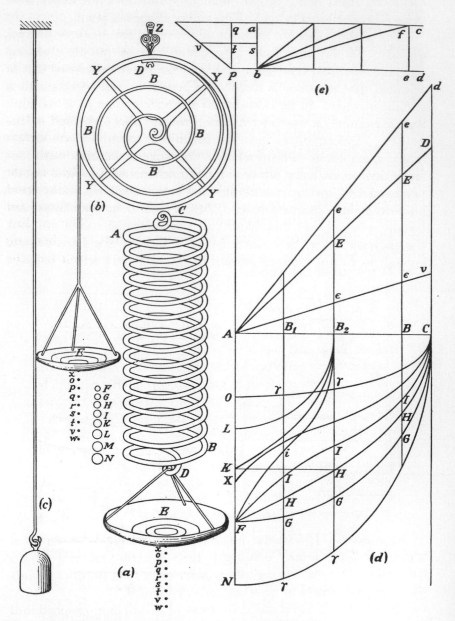

Fig. 2.3. Devices used in Hooke's experiments. [From Timoshenko, *History of Strength of Materials*, McGraw-Hill.]

members, stress being proportional to strain does not imply that stress is proportional to load. This will be discussed later.

The author does not know of any method for measuring stress directly. In the laboratory a specimen can be put in a testing machine, the load read on a dial, and the stress calculated if it is assumed that the stress is distributed across the test specimen in a certain manner. In an odd-shaped member or one in a machine that is running, stress determination by the above method is impossible. Deformations must be measured and the stress determined from these measurements. Everyone is familiar with deformations in ordinary life even though articles such as automobile tires and bed springs are accepted without thinking about their load-deflection characteristics. Deformations in machines are usually so small that they cannot be seen with the naked eye, but the engineer knows that when a load is applied, the parts deform enough to set up internal stresses in the members which balance

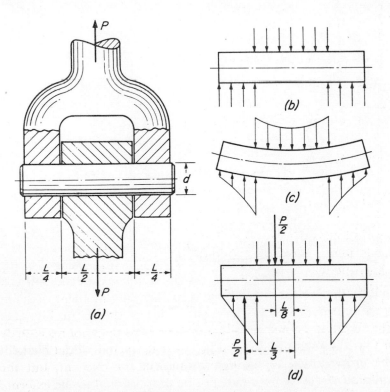

Fig. 2.4. Knuckle joint.

the externally applied load. If the members cannot balance the external load, one or more of them fails. Deformations are easier to visualize than stresses and for this reason stress problems can sometimes be analyzed by first considering the strains. This will be illustrated by an example.

If the parts of the knuckle joint, Fig. 2.4(a), are accurately made and the load P is very small, the load distribution on the pin will be approximately that shown in Fig. 2.4(b). An increase in load will increase the deformation and shift the load as shown in Fig. 2.4(c), the change in distribution being greater at the ends than in the center because of greater deviation from the original configuration of the pin. The simplified distribution shown at Fig. 2.4(d) is often used to determine the bending stress in the pin.

The L/d ratio of the knuckle pin for equal strength in bending and direct shear can be found as follows. The stress due to bending is

$$s = \frac{Mc}{I} = \frac{\frac{P}{2}\left(\frac{L}{3} - \frac{L}{8}\right)32}{\pi d^3} \qquad (2.4)$$

The stress due to direct shear is

$$s_s = \frac{P}{A} = \frac{2P}{\pi d^2} \qquad (2.5)$$

Using the relation $s = 2s_s$ and equating gives

$$L = \tfrac{6}{5}\, d \qquad (2.6)$$

If the L/d ratio is less than this, the pin will not fail in bending.

It must be remembered that the assumed load distribution shown in Fig. 2.4(d) is approximately correct for a pin in an average knuckle joint. If the L/d ratio is large or small or if the fork is flexible, the load distribution may be somewhat different.

It can be seen that the direct shear stress is proportional to the load, i.e., it follows Hooke's law, but in bending the load shifts as the pull on the joint is increased and the bending moment does not increase in proportion to the pull. This is shown in Fig. 2.5.

The fact that a material follows Hooke's law does not necessarily mean that the member does. The stress in an individual element will be proportional to the deformation of the element, but the deformation of the element may not be proportional to the external load that deforms the entire member.

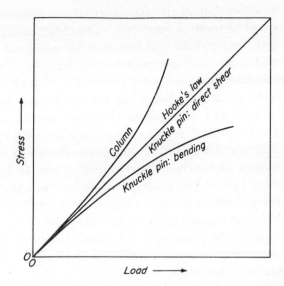

Fig. 2.5. Stress-load curves for knuckle pin and column.

The load-deflection relationship for a ball bearing does not follow Hooke's law. Under a light load the contact area between a ball and the race is small, and as the load is increased, the area of contact increases, producing a stiffening effect. In some machine

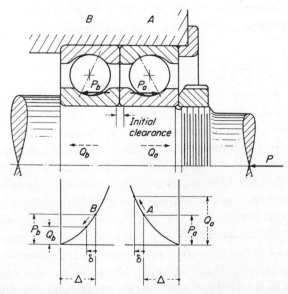

Fig. 2.6. Preloaded ball bearings.

tools and scientific apparatus where great accuracy is desired, preloading of ball bearings is used to eliminate any initial looseness and to eliminate the first part of the load deflection curve where the deflection is relatively large compared with the load.

The pair of preloaded bearings shown in Fig. 2.6 has the grooves in the races offset axially so that when the outer races are brought together there is a small clearance between the inner races. When the inner races are forced together by tightening the lock nut, a thrust load on each inner race is produced, shown by P_b and P_a, which corresponds to the initial deflection Δ shown in the load-deflection curves below the bearings. The external load P causes the inner races of both bearings to move to the left an amount δ which increases P_a to Q_a and reduces P_b to Q_b. The reduction of P_b is a factor that helps to keep δ small. A state of equilibrium is reached when $Q_a - Q_b = P$. Preloaded bearings of this type also reduce deflections due to radial loads.

Most members follow Hooke's law which makes calculations more simple; this is especially true in vibrations. The simplest vibrating system, Fig. 2.7(a), consists of a mass and a linear spring (follows Hooke's law) which causes the mass to vibrate with simple harmonic motion. The same holds for the disk and shaft, Fig. 2.7(b), for both torsional and lateral vibration. The differential equation that expresses the motion of a mass on a linear spring has conveniently been called a *linear* differential equation.

2.4. *Factor of Safety*[1]

The factor of safety is often specified by a numerical value, but its meaning is much broader than this. The numerical value which is used when failure due to breaking or permanent deformation is the criterion will be discussed first. For static loading with brittle materials, the working stress is usually obtained by dividing the ultimate strength by the factor of safety, while for ductile materials the yield strength is used, and when the load is completely reversed, the endurance limit is used. If the factor of safety is defined as the ratio of the failure load to the expected operating load, the above

---

[1] For other discussions see P. H. Black, *Machine Design*, 2nd ed. (New York: McGraw-Hill Book Co., Inc., 1955) and G. H. Howell, "Factors of Safety," *Machine Design*, July 12, 1956.

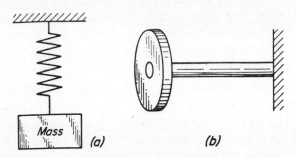

Fig. 2.7. Vibrating systems.

procedure is not always correct because not all members follow Hooke's law. In columns, Fig. 2.5, the calculations must be based on loads rather than stresses if the full value of the factor of safety is to be realized.

Aluminum does not have an endurance limit, i.e., in the plot of the failure stress versus cycles, the curve does not level off but continues to go down. Aluminum parts subjected to fatigue loading must be designed for limited life. Another way of thinking about it is that the factor of safety decreases with operating time.

A machine that is worn to the extent that it no longer fulfills its function can be considered to have failed. Wear is considered from the standpoint of life. If it is expected that a machine will become obsolete in a certain number of years, it is necessary to design the machine so that the wear will not be excessive in this length of time. If this is not feasible, the machine should be designed to facilitate replacement or remachining of the worn parts. Brake linings and drums are an example of this type.

Certain members in some machines must be designed for both strength and stiffness. If the shaft in a gear reducer is flexible enough to cause excessive wear of the gears, the shaft can be considered to have failed in one of its functions.

A machine that is designed with the same factor of safety throughout is often considered to be an ideal machine, but it is not always as simple as this. In a machine where there may be momentary overloads of undetermined value, the ductile parts may be designed with one factor of safety, the brittle parts may be designed with a higher factor of safety, the rigidity of the parts may be just adequate for normal operation, and the design for wear may be based on an assumed life.

The broad meaning of factor of safety will be amplified in the following discussion of safe failure.

2.5. *Safe Failure*

Although safe failure (also known as *progressive failure*) is not a new concept, it has recently been broadened by intensive study and application in the aircraft industry. In aircraft design every effort is put forth to prevent failure, but because there will always be some failure, the concept of safe failure is used wherever possible. One method of safe failure is to use several small parts instead of a single large one. If one part fails, the airplane will not fall apart or crash but will continue to operate with a reduced factor of safety for a limited time. Since a crack in one member of a riveted structure will not progress to another member, a riveted structure is designed for safe failure if it continues to function after any one of the members has failed. Frequent inspection is necessary to locate the parts that have failed or have started to fail.

Safety devices such as shear pins and slip couplings can be included in the concept of safe failure. In many machines where failure would not cause personal injury, the purpose of these devices is to prevent damage to machines or long and costly shutdowns.

2.6. *Stress Concentration*

Stress concentration within the elastic limit might just as well be called *strain concentration* since stress and strain always exist concurrently. In Fig. 2.8(a) there is a region on each side of the hole that is strained (stressed) to a higher value than the surrounding material. Assume that in this case the stress is twice as high as the nominal stress. Assume further that the machinist, in locating the hole, made long scribe lines that extended beyond the hole to be drilled. The scratch will introduce stress concentration in a very small volume along its length. This small volume lies within the relatively large volume of highly stressed material at the edge of the hole. If the stress concentration factor for the scratch is 3, then the overall stress concentration factor is $2 \times 3 = 6$.

In Fig. 2.8(b) a highly magnified section of a rough surface and a scratch are shown. In this case the stress concentration factors of surface and scratch do not necessarily combine; the scratch may

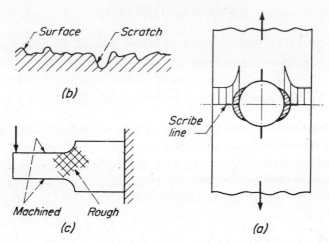

Fig. 2.8. Three causes of stress concentration.

remove the surface in that volume near the surface where its stress concentration applies. If this is the case, the larger of the two factors would be used. In some cases, such as decarburization, the surface is weakened due to a chemical change. In a case like this, the scratch might or might not extend into the stronger material below the surface. The partial machining of a member with a rough surface, Fig. 2.8(c), leaves feather edges that can produce high stress concentrations. If a member of this type is to be subjected to cyclic loading, the feather edges should be removed. The following quotation[1] shows the importance of stress concentration in design:

"The story of these failures and of analogous failures in other fields, is a tale of notches, nicks, keyways, oil holes, screw threads, scratches, rough surfaces, quenching cracks, grinding cracks, sharp changes in section, thin outstanding fins, poor fillets, tool marks, inclusions in the metal, corrosion pits, and the like, i.e., some localized nucleus from which failure started. Big notches, little notches, sharp notches, round notches, deep scratches, or shallow scratches, all are nuclei of varying severity. Some of these cannot be avoided; when a screw thread or an oil hole is

[1] Staff of the Battelle Memorial Institute, *Prevention of the Failure of Metals under Repeated Stress* (New York: John Wiley & Sons, Inc., 1941). This study is continued in Gordon, Grover and Jackson, "The Fatigue of Metals and Structures" (Washington: United States Government Printing Office, Superintendent of Public Documents, 1954).

needed, it must be used but there is no need to use the worst kind of a screw thread, the oil hole need not be rough nor its edges unrelieved, nor need the oil hole always be put in the worst location as far as fatigue is concerned.

"Failed parts, especially those of aircraft, usually are returned for metallurgical examination to learn whether anything was wrong with the metal itself. In 99 cases out of 100, the examination shows that the metal was high grade and failed simply because it *had* to fail under the conditions of local repeated loading that were imposed upon it at some particular, tiny spot. The metal was obeying the laws of nature.

"The unbearable conditions imposed upon it were created, not by the inherent requirements of design, but through some slip of the designer, the machinist, or the inspector, who failed to recognize that unbearable conditions were being set up. He did not appreciate the natural laws involved.

"These natural laws have been revealed to a considerable, though not yet to a complete, extent and have been discussed in many articles in technical journals and in a few books. This literature, however, is seldom accessible to the designer, the machinist, or the inspector, and is often couched in such technical language that it is not very clear to them.

"Yet nature exacts the penalty when her laws are violated — ignorance of the laws is no excuse to her. Moreover, to the family of a pilot who has been killed through the failure of a part which was obeying nature's laws, it is cold comfort to know that the slip made by the designer, the machinist, or the inspector, was innocently made, because no one sufficiently emphasized the natural laws that came into play."

The figure of 99 per cent is not surprising when it is remembered that the stress is usually maximum on the outside of the member. In a simple member that is subjected to tension or compression, it is assumed that the stress is uniform across the section, but if there is bending or torsion present, the stress is a maximum on the outside. A flaw in the interior of a member can produce a stress that is higher than that on the surface, but these internal stress raisers are rare compared with those found on the surface.

2.7. *Poisson's Ratio*

Poisson's ratio is the relation between the strain perpendicular to the line of action of the stress and the strain parallel to the line of action of the stress. If a material did not change in volume when loaded, Poisson's ratio for small deflections would be 0.5. This can

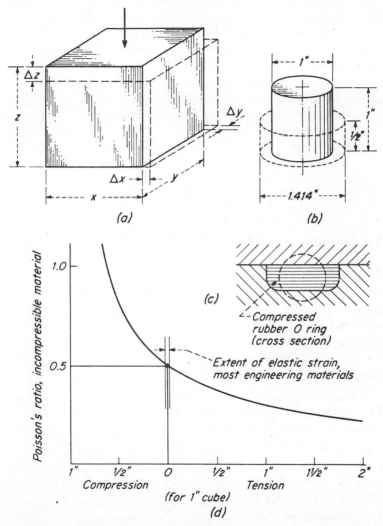

Fig. 2.9. (a) Cube for determining Poisson's ratio; (b) rubber bumper; (c) compression O ring; (d) Poisson's ratio for large deflections.

be shown as follows. Assume that the cube shown in Fig. 2.9(a) is uniformly loaded on the top which produces the vertical deflection Δz and the side deflections Δx and Δy. If the material is incompressible, the final volume will be equal to the original volume, or

$$xyz = (z - \Delta z)(x + \Delta x)(y + \Delta y)$$

Letting x and y equal z, Δy equal Δx, and dropping terms of higher order, gives

$$\frac{\Delta z}{z} = 2 \cdot \frac{\Delta x}{x} \quad \text{or} \quad \mu = \frac{\Delta x/x}{\Delta z/z} = 0.5$$

where μ is Poisson's ratio. The terms are of higher order only if Δx, Δy, and Δz are small, which must be the case for most engineering materials if plastic deformation is to be avoided. Approximate values of Poisson's ratio for several materials are shown in Table 2.1. All materials occupy a smaller volume when compressed although some, rubber for example, are very nearly incompressible.

TABLE 2.1

Material	Poisson's Ratio
Aluminum	0.33
Brass	0.35
Cast iron	0.25
Concrete	0.10
Copper	0.35
Cork	0.00
Glass	0.24
Rubber	0.49
Steel	0.33

If the deflection is large and is based on an original dimension, Poisson's ratio is a variable as shown in Fig. 2.9(d). As Δz approaches z, the sides push out to infinity giving an infinite value for Poisson's ratio, and if the cube is subjected to tension, Poisson's ratio approaches zero as Δz approaches infinity. This is a hypothetical case since all solids have an elastic limit. Poisson's ratio can be taken as a constant for most engineering materials.

Deflection calculations for rubber parts are usually based on volume. If the rubber bumper, Fig. 2.9(b), is to fit into a hole after it has been compressed to half its height, the hole must be at least 1.414 in. in diameter. The diameter of the hole based on a Poisson's ratio value of 0.49 would be 1.245 in. The volume of the groove that receives the rubber O ring, Fig. 2.9(c), must exceed that of the O ring if there are small cavities into which the rubber cannot be forced without destroying it or producing high loads.

The required groove angle of a V-belt sheave depends on the radius of the pulley as shown in Fig. 2.10. When the belt is bent around the sheave, the outer portion is in tension and becomes narrower, while the inner portion is in compression and becomes broader. The new cross section is accommodated by using a groove angle θ' which is smaller than θ, the angle of the unbent belt.

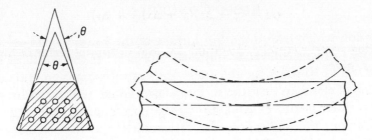

Fig. 2.10. V belt, showing effect of Poisson's ratio.

A steel beam behaves in the same manner as the V-belt, but with the usual proportions, the lateral deflections are small and are neglected.

A method of determining Poisson's ratio is shown in Fig. 2.11. The change in the slope of the sides of the beam resulting from the addition of weights in the pan, is measured by pointer P on the scale which is attached to the rod UT. In this case the top of the beam is

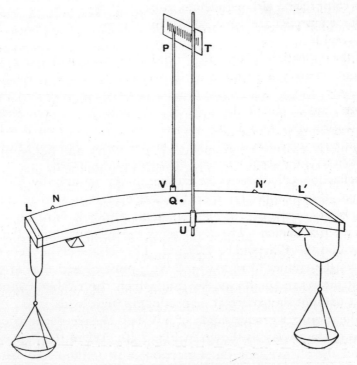

Fig. 2.11. A method of determining Poisson's ratio. [Searle, *Experimental Elasticity*, Cambridge University Press]

in tension which causes the top surface of the beam to be concave upward. This is called an anticlastic surface. If the width of the beam is 8 to 10 times the thickness, the lateral expansion and contraction of elements near the surface is prevented, which results in a slightly stiffer member. An approximate correction can be made by multiplying the deflection as determined by the elementary equations, by $(1 - \mu^2)$.

The problem of nuts loosening under variable loading has been investigated by many competent engineers, but the cause was not found until J. N. Goodier,[1] who was an expert in mechanics of materials and familiar with Hooke's law and Poisson's ratio, investigated the problem. Goodier, knowing that stress was present, knew that deformations were also present, and this proved to be the key to the problem.

If a nut and bolt fit together perfectly before loading, they will deform as shown in Fig. 2.12(a) when loaded. The bolt is stretched and the nut is compressed causing a few threads at the bottom to carry most of the load. Points A and B on the bolt and nut coincide when the load is at a minimum, and separate when the load is increased. This radial sliding of B relative to A results from the bending of threads, the lateral expansion of the bottom of the nut, and the contraction of the bolt due to Poisson's ratio. Kinetic friction replaces static friction.

If a block is placed on an incline, Fig. 2.12(b), and pulled to the right by means of a flexible cord, it will slide downhill due to the component of the weight that acts down the incline. The same thing occurs in the nut and bolt under variable loading as shown in Fig. 2.12(c). Instead of B sliding back and forth radially, it moves up the helical surface (at point B the force is acting up against the bolt thread) in a zigzag path.

The elastic stop nut, Fig. 2.12(d), has a fiber collar f which is set in a recess in the nut and grips the bolt when the nut is tightened. This provides a frictional force which resists the unscrewing torque at the lower threads. This ring would not be effective at the bottom of the nut where there is relative motion between the nut and bolt

---

[1] J. N. Goodier and R. J. Sweeney, "Loosening by Vibration of Threaded Fastenings," *Mechanical Engineering*, December, 1945, and J. N. Goodier, "The Distribution of Load on the Thread of Screws," *Journal of Applied Mechanics, Trans. ASME*, **62**, 1940, p. A-10.

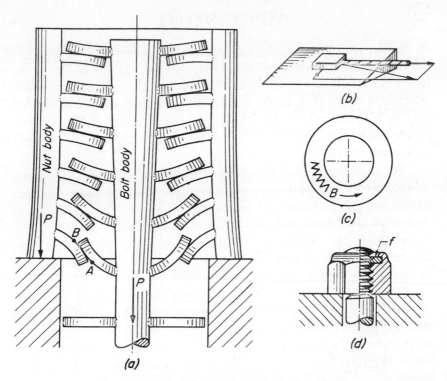

Fig. 2.12. Deformation of loaded bolt and nut.

threads, as can be seen in Fig. 2.12(b). The application of a vertical force to the block (e.g., increasing the weight of the block) will not prevent it from moving down the incline. The required pull on the cord will be greater, but the component of force down the incline will be increased in the same proportion.

Up to a certain point, the tightening of the nut will tend to reduce the unscrewing action, not because of increased pressure between the threads, but because of reduced variable loading which reduces the relative sliding. This will be discussed in the chapter on optimum design.

A recent investigation[1] of forging-hammer anvils has shown that Poisson's ratio is responsible for many failures. A second investigation[2] using a model has shown that the use of a redesigned key will

---

[1] W. J. Eding, "An Investigation of Forging-Hammer Anvil Failures," Master's Thesis, Michigan State University, 1953.

[2] J. R. Ritzema, "A Model Study of Sow Block Key Design," Master's Thesis, Michigan State University, 1955.

reduce the stress at the critical section to less than half of the former value.

Anvils for large hammers cost from forty to seventy thousand dollars, and failure requires that the hammer be shut down for several weeks. Failure of ten or more anvils a year in one plant led to the first investigation. Fig. 2.13 shows an anvil with sow block

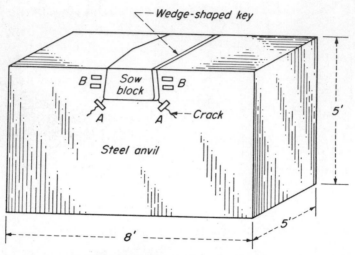

Fig. 2.13. Forging hammer anvil.

which carries the lower die, and wedge-shaped key which is driven into place to prevent the sow block from moving relative to the anvil. Variable resistance wire strain gages placed at A showed that the stress was high, as was expected, since failure occurred here. Strain gages at B showed that there was compressive stress each time a blow was struck.

In the test arrangement, Fig. 2.15, a falling weight was used to produce the impact on the model anvil which is shown more clearly in Fig. 2.14.

The variable loading, indicated by AB on the load-deflection diagram for the conventional key, Fig. 2.16(a), is superimposed on the static load, OA, which results from driving the key in place. A key that acts as a softer spring will not transmit as much of the expansion load of the sow block to the anvil as will a stiff spring. A softer key can be made either by using a material with a low modulus of elasticity, or by using a steel key that is designed for flexibility as was used on this model, Fig. 2.16(b). This key was

Fig. 2.14. Forging hammer anvil in static testing machine. [Courtesy R. L. Vanderslice]

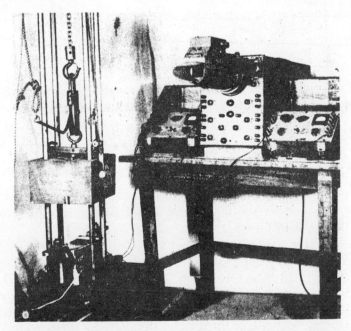

Fig. 2.15. Forging hammer anvil in impact testing machine. [Courtesy R. L. Vanderslice]

driven into place to produce the same initial load as the solid key and then, under hammering, produced only 40 per cent as high a stress at the fillet as was found with the conventional key.

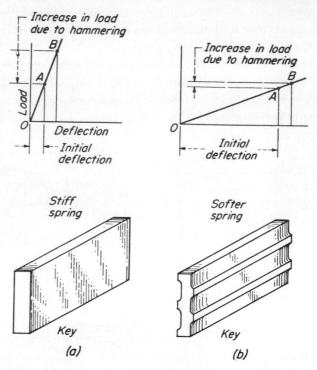

Fig. 2.16. (a) Conventional sow block key; (b) redesigned key.

This is a very simple solution, but like the loosening of nuts under variable loading, it defied analysis for many years because the investigators who worked on the problem did not consider deflections.

2.8. *Superposition*

The principle of *superposition*, which is generally valid for bodies following Hooke's law, means that the stress or deflection of any element in a body subjected to any combination of forces, moments, and torques can be determined by calculating the stress or deflection for each force, moment, or torque and then adding them vectorially.

The stress in the vertical portion of the C-frame, Fig. 2.17(a), is determined by the principle of superposition,

$$s = \frac{P}{A} \pm \frac{(Pa)}{I/c} \tag{2.7}$$

The total deflection, δ, of the end of the C-frame is the sum of the individual deflections, δ_1 due to stretching of the vertical portion of the C-frame, δ_2 due to bending of the vertical portion, and δ_3 due to the bending of the horizontal portion.

Superposition can also be used to determine stresses and deflections in the member shown in Fig. 2.17(b). In this analysis it will be convenient to resolve force P_2 into vertical and horizontal components and to consider them separately.

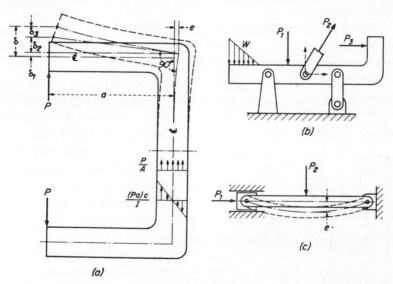

Fig. 2.17. Members (a) and (b) can be analyzed by using superposition principle; member (c) cannot be so analyzed.

If the rod, Fig. 2.17(c), is slender enough to act as a column, i.e., e becomes large enough to make an appreciable moment arm for P_1, superposition cannot be used. The sum of the stresses determined by considering P_1 and P_2 separately will be less than the stress due to P_1 and P_2 acting simultaneously. The reason for this difference is that P_1 and P_2 acting simultaneously produce a larger e than P_1 acting alone. In Fig. 2.17(a), e is small compared with a and therefore does not appreciably affect the moment.

It was shown that the bending stress in the knuckle pin, Fig. 2.4(a), is not proportional to the load. However, superposition can be used to determine stress and deflection for the final loading shown in Fig. 2.4(d). Nonlinearity was accounted for by using past experience to arrive at an approximate load distribution.

2.9. *Strain Energy*

The principle of conservation of energy states that in an isolated system, energy can be redistributed or changed in form but cannot be created or destroyed. An isolated system is one in which no bodies or conditions outside the system have any effect on the bodies within the system. Conservation of energy, like Newton's laws of motion, is not subject to an analytical proof but is rather the result of observations.

When only mechanical energy is involved, it is in the form of potential energy due to height, potential energy due to elastic deformation, and kinetic energy. It is not necessary to have an isolated system to make an analysis. If the original energy in the system is known and after a time t the input and output energies are known and the loss due to friction can be determined, the remaining energy must be accounted for in the three forms listed above.

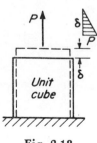

Potential energy due to height and kinetic energy are seldom overlooked by the designer, but elastic strain energy, except for such obvious members as springs, is sometimes not given the consideration that it deserves and will therefore be discussed in detail.

The modulus of resilience of a material is the elastic energy stored by a unit volume when it is loaded to the elastic limit in tension. In Fig. 2.18, the work done by the uniformly increasing force P acting through the distance δ, is

Fig. 2.18

$$u = \frac{P\delta}{2}$$

Substituting $\delta = P/E$ in the above expression gives

$$u = \frac{P^2}{2E}$$

which, for the yield stress, becomes

$$u = \frac{s_y^2}{2E} \tag{2.8}$$

The units are inch-pounds per cubic inch.

The modulus of resilience for shear can be obtained from consideration of a unit cube, or a thin walled tube in torsion, Fig. 2.19.

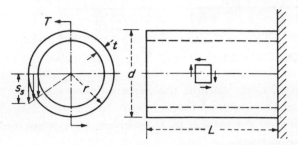

Fig. 2.19. Hollow shaft for determination of strain energy in shear.

For the thin walled tube it is assumed that s_s is constant across the thickness t and that the polar moment of inertia is $\pi d t r^2$. The external work done in twisting the tube is

$$u_s = \frac{T\theta}{2}$$

Placing the values of $\theta = TL/JG$ and $T = s_{sy}J/r$ in the above equation gives

$$u_s = \frac{s_{sy}^2 \pi r t L}{G}$$

Dividing this by the volume of the tube, $2r\pi t L$, gives the work per unit volume

$$u_s = \frac{s_{sy}^2}{2G}. \tag{2.9}$$

Similarly, the expression derived for a solid rod is

$$u_s = \frac{s_{sy}^2}{4G} \tag{2.10}$$

This can be considered as the average work for all elements.

To prevent buckling and to provide material for strength and energy absorption, the thickness of the tube must be appreciable, although in many applications it can be relatively small compared with d. For all practical applications the average modulus of resilience in shear for a hollow shaft lies between the two values given above.

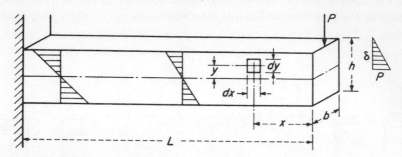

Fig. 2.20. Determination of beam deflection, using strain energy.

The following example shows how elastic strain energy can be used to determine deflections. In Fig. 2.20 the external work done on the cantilever is

$$U = \frac{P\delta}{2}$$

This must equal the strain energy in the cantilever. The stress varies linearly from zero at the neutral axis to a maximum on the outer surface, and linearly from zero at the free end to a maximum at the fixed end. The strain energy in an element $dx\ dy\ b$ is

$$dU = \frac{s^2}{2E}b\ dx\ dy$$

Placing the value of $s = Pxy/I$ in this expression gives

$$dU = \frac{P^2 b x^2 y^2}{2EI^2}\ dx\ dy$$

This expression, when integrated over the top half of the beam and multiplied by 2, can be equated to the external work:

$$\frac{1}{2}\ P\delta = \frac{P^2 b}{EI^2} \int_0^L \int_0^{h/2} x^2 y^2\ dx\ dy$$

$$= \frac{P^2 b}{EI^2}\left(\frac{x^3}{3}\right)_0^L\left(\frac{y^3}{3}\right)_0^{h/2} = \frac{P^2}{EI^2} \cdot \frac{bh^3}{12} \cdot \frac{L^3}{6} = \frac{P^2 L^3}{6EI}$$

or

$$\delta = \frac{PL^3}{3EI}$$

Several examples of strain energy capacity in machine components are now explained to help in the understanding of their design. In Fig. 2.21(a) the rod stretches an amount δ due to load P. The rod in Fig. 2.21(b) is made from a material having the same modulus of elasticity and twice the yield strength of that in (a), hence the cross sectional area need be only half as large. For the same load, the deformation will be twice as large. The rod shown in Fig. 2.21(c) is made of the same material as the rod shown in Fig. 2.21(b). For the same load P the deformation will be 4δ.

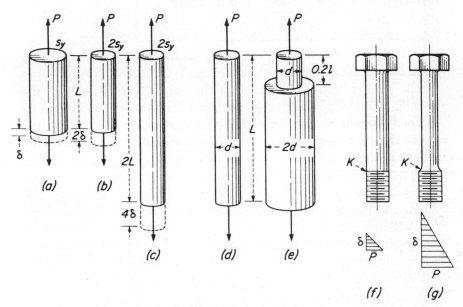

Fig. 2.21. Deflection of several members in tension.

Equation (2.8) can be used to verify this. Rods (a) and (c) have equal volumes and equal loads P but the stress in (c) is twice that in (a).

The adding of material to a uniformly stressed member in a manner that reduces the stress in a portion of the member, reduces the strain energy capacity. The strain energy capacity of the rod shown in Fig. 2.21(d) is

$$U = \frac{P\delta}{2} = \frac{P^2L}{2AE}$$

The capacity of the member shown in Fig. 2.21(e), assuming that it is made of the same material as the rod in Fig. 2.21(d) and neglecting stress concentration, is

$$U = \frac{P^2 0.2L}{2AE} + \frac{P^2 0.8L}{2 \times 4AE} = \frac{0.4P^2L}{2AE}$$

It has 40 per cent of the capacity of the rod shown in Fig. 2.21(d).
If the stress concentration factor at the change of section is 2, and it
is included, the allowable load will be reduced to half its former
value which will reduce the energy absorbing capacity to 10 per
cent of that of the rod shown in Fig. 2.21(d).

The bolts shown in Fig. 2.21 are a practical example of this.
The standard bolt shown in Fig. 2.21(f) corresponds to Fig. 2.21(e),
the stress concentration and the root area limits the load so that the
body of the bolt is not highly stressed and the deflection is therefore
small. In Fig. 2.21(g) the body of the bolt is turned down to the
root diameter. This reduces the stress concentration which permits
a larger load to be applied. The reduction in the diameter of the
shank also increases the deflection-load rate which is indicated by
the steeper slope of the hypotenuse of the energy triangle.

The factors to be considered for obtaining a maximum energy
absorbing capacity in a member can be summarized as follows: use
a material having high strength, use a material with a low modulus
of elasticity (this is often not feasible), and design as closely as
possible for uniform stress throughout the member. Regions of low
stress reduce the deformation for a given load and therefore the
strain energy is less (see discussion of members (d) and (e) in
Fig. 2.21). If the desired capacity cannot be obtained using these
factors, then the volume of the material must be increased in such a
manner that the load or deflection is increased.

Design for high strain energy capacity is not always necessary,
but is usually of importance in cases where impact or momentary
overloads may occur. Good design requires efficient use of material
and a minimum of stress concentration. This tends to increase the
strain energy capacity of a member. When weight is a major factor,
unusual designs can be employed, e.g., a coil spring made from a
tube will absorb more energy than one of the same weight that is
made from a solid rod.

In most applications a machine member has failed when it has
been permanently deformed, although there are numerous cases
where this is not true. Statically loaded members that have un-
avoidable stress raisers, if made of a ductile material, are not
harmed when small regions are plastically deformed during initial
loading. This often occurs at the root of threads in screw fastenings
when they are initially tightened.

Fig. 2.22(a) illustrates the difference between a strong and a tough steel. Toughness is the ability of a material to absorb strain energy up to fracture. The stronger material will absorb more elastic strain energy, area *OBC*, than the tougher steel, *OAD*, but

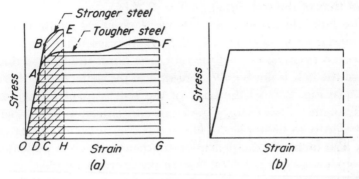

Fig. 2.22. (a) Stress-strain diagrams for high strength and tough steels; (b) idealized stress-strain diagram.

when the plastic region is included, the tougher steel has a larger capacity, *OAFG*, compared with the stronger steel, *OABEH*. Stress-strain curves are often idealized, Fig. 2.22(b), in order to simplify derivations and calculations.

In Fig. 2.23, assume that while the drive is operating, the sliding block *C* jams and stops *instantly*. This is of course impossible, but it is on the side of safety to make this assumption when making an energy analysis. The remaining elements in the drive will not stop instantly but will continue to turn until the kinetic energy in the system is absorbed in the form of elastic strain energy, or elastic strain energy and plastic work, or rupture of one of the members.

The elastic strain energy that a machine can absorb can be calculated by analyzing the individual members, but in some cases, because of complex shapes and uncertain load distribution, this can be considered only as an approximation. The elastic strain energy for the drive shown here can be determined experimentally as follows, fix member *C* and measure the angular deflection of the motor shaft at *E* as increments of torque are applied. The plot of this data would probably be similar to the curve *OAB*, Fig. 2.24(a). The low spring rate for the first portion of the curve, *OA*, is usually present because of bearings, meshing gear teeth, keys, and pin connections. After an appreciable torque has been applied, firm contact is made on these elements and the spring rate increases as shown by the portion of the curve, *AB*.

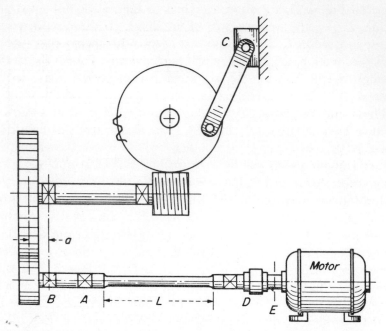

Fig. 2.23. Machine with shaft reduced in diameter to absorb strain energy in the plastic region.

The area *OABE*, Fig. 2.24(a), represents the elastic strain energy that the system can absorb when the weakest element has reached the yield stress. If this is not sufficient to absorb the kinetic energy and it is not feasible to increase the elastic area,

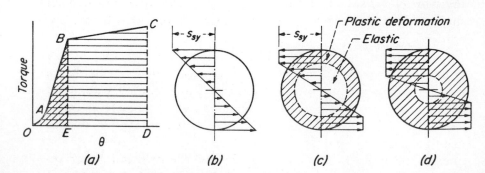

Fig. 2.24. (a) Torque-deflection diagrams for machine shown in Fig. 2.23; (b) stress distribution in the shaft at the yield point; (c) and (d) stress distribution in the plastic region.

one of the members can be designed to dissipate the energy plastically. In Fig. 2.23, the shaft attached to the motor has a turned portion, L, i.e., the weakest part of the drive. If there is sufficient volume in portion L, the portion will absorb the energy plastically. Plastic absorption of the energy will permanently deform the shaft, although it will function for a limited period before it has to be replaced.

The nature of plastic deformation in a ductile shaft in torsion is shown in Figs. 2.24(b), (c), and (d). The elastic stress distribution shown at (b) corresponds to point B on the curve shown at (a). Further angular twisting of the shaft will produce a region of plastic deformation shown at (c), and the stress distribution, assuming the idealized stress-strain curve, Fig. 2.22(b), will be as shown. Fig. 2.24(d) represents the shaft after it has been subjected to further angular twist. It can be seen that the internal torque at (c) is greater than that at (b), and at (d) it is greater than at (c). This increase in internal torque of the shaft over the length L is one reason why the portion of the diagram BC, Fig. 2.24(a), is not horizontal. The other reason is that the increasing plastic torque in the shaft produces additional elastic deformation in the other members of the machine. It must be remembered that the diagram shown at (a) represents the deformation of the entire machine.

If, in addition to preventing rupture of a member, it is desired that the drive be capable of functioning for a limited time, it is necessary to control the nature of the plastic deformation. As shown in Fig. 2.23, there is no bending in the shaft over the length L. If bearing A is removed, there will be bending in the region L due to the gear tooth load which has a lever arm a. Plastic bending of the shaft might cause the gears to bind and prevent subsequent operation.

A slip coupling at D would serve the same purpose, and if jamming is expected from time to time, one would probably be installed. However, in an airplane, frequent jamming would not be tolerated, and the offending members would be redesigned to lessen the possibility of jamming. The shaft as designed in this example cannot be tampered with or improperly adjusted. If the unexpected happens and member C jams, the operator, after relieving the jamming, will find the drive intact and capable of functioning for at least a limited time. This design can be considered as an example of design for safe failure.

2.10. *Saint-Venant's Principle*[1]

This principle states that if the forces acting on a small portion of the surface of an elastic body are replaced by another statically equivalent system of forces acting on the same portion of the surface, this redistribution of loading may produce substantial local changes in the stresses but has a negligible effect on the stresses at distances which are large in comparison with the linear dimensions of the surface on which the forces are changed.

According to Saint-Venant's principle, two different distributions of force having the same resultant and acting on a small part of an elastic body will produce the same stress except in the immediate neighborhood of the load. If one of these distributions is reversed and combined with the other, there will be zero stress except in this neighborhood. The combined loads are self-equilibrating, and the principle is in fact equivalent to the statement that a self-equilibrating distribution of force on a small part of an elastic solid produces only local stress. The following discussion should make this clear.

In Fig. 2.25(a), a cantilever is loaded along a knife edge by the force P which will produce bending stress near the support as shown. If, instead of force P acting on the knife edge, an equal force, P', acts on the pin as shown, the stress near the support will be the same as for force P.

In Fig. 2.25(b), two loads, P' reversed and P, act on the beam. It can be shown from energy considerations that no work is done except in a small region near the loads. If s denotes the order of magnitude (average) of the force per unit area, and a represents a linear dimension of the loaded part, the unit strain components are of order s/E and the displacements within the loaded part are of the order sa/E. The work done (average force $\times$ displacement) is of order $a^2/2 \cdot sa/E = s^2a^3/2E$. The stress components of order s imply strain energy of order $s^2/2E$ per unit volume. Dividing the total strain energy by the strain energy for a unit volume gives the volume that is affected by the loads P and $-P'$.

$$\frac{s^2a^3/2E}{s^2/2E} = a^3$$

---

[1] This discussion is based on S. Timoshenko and J. N. Goodier, *Theory of Elasticity*, 2nd ed. (New York: McGraw-Hill Book Co., Inc., 1951).

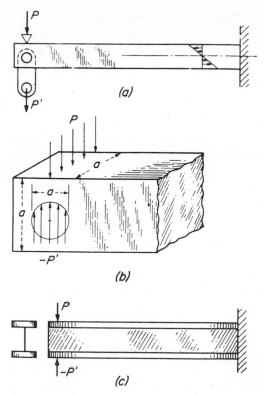

Fig. 2.25. (a) Alternate methods of loading a beam (P or P') do not affect stress distribution except in the region near the load; (b) two loads, P' reversed and P, acting on the beam; (c) forces P and P' will produce stress in the thin web over a considerable portion of its length.

Fig. 2.25. (d) Isochromatic fringe pattern of a beam under pure bending. The parallel fringes in the region of pure bending affirm elementary beam theory; the photo is a verification of St. Venant's principle. [Reproduced by permission from G. H. Lee, *An Introduction to Experimental Stress Analysis* (New York: John Wiley & Sons, Inc., 1950]

If $-P'$ relieves all of the stress in the beam due to P except for this small region of dimension a, then the removal of $-P'$ will bring about a stress distribution in the beam that follows the nominal equation, $s = Mc/I$, except for the small region near the load P.

It has been assumed here that the body is of solid form. If it is not of solid form, as for instance a beam with a very thin web or a thin cylindrical shell, a self-equilibrating distribution of force may be felt at distances many times the depth or diameter. In Fig. 2.25(c), it can be seen that the forces P and P' will produce stress in the thin web over a considerable portion of its length.

Saint-Venant's principle explains why notches, holes, fillets, etc., usually increase the stress in the member only in the neighborhood of the discontinuity.

2.11. *Stress Waves in Elastic Solids*[1]

Up to the present, it has been assumed that the stress distribution throughout a member immediately follows the application of a force or a change in force, but this is not always true. The action of a suddenly applied force or a change in force is not transmitted at once to all parts of the body. At the beginning the remote portions of the body remain undisturbed, and deformations produced by the force are propagated through the body in the form of elastic waves.

The velocity of propagation of waves in prismatical bars can be obtained from elementary considerations. Assume that a uniformly distributed compressive stress is suddenly applied to the left end of a prismatical bar, Fig. 2.26, and then maintained constant. It will

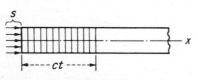

Fig. 2.26. Stress wave.

produce at the first instant a uniform compression of an infinitely thin layer at the left end of the bar. This compression will be transmitted to the adjacent layer, and so on. A wave of compression begins to travel along the bar with a certain velocity c, and, after a time interval t, a portion of the bar of length ct will be compressed and the remaining portion will be at rest in an unstressed condition.

---

[1] A part of this discussion is based on S. Timoshenko and J. N. Goodier, *Theory of Elasticity*, 2nd ed. (New York: McGraw-Hill Book Co., Inc., 1951).

The velocity of wave propagation c should be distinguished from the velocity v, given to particles in the compressed zone of the bar by the compressive forces. This can be visualized by considering the crude analogy of the freight train. Assume that the engine of the stationary train, Fig. 2.27, starts moving to the right with a velocity v. The engine sends a tension wave along the train by picking up the cars one by one, and if the slack in the couplings is small, the wave will travel the entire length of the train while the engine is

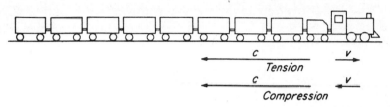

Fig. 2.27. Stress wave analogy.

moving forward only a few inches. In a tension wave the particle velocity is opposite to that of the wave velocity. If, instead of going forward, the engine had backed, a compressive wave would have travelled the length of the train in the same manner. Note that in a compressive wave the particle velocity and wave velocity move in the same direction.

The velocity of the particles v, Fig. 2.26, can be found by taking into account the fact that the compressed zone (shaded in the figure) shortens due to compressive stress s by the amount $(s/E)ct$. Hence the velocity of the left end of the bar, equal to the velocity of particles in the compressed zone, is

$$v = \frac{(s/E)ct}{t} = \frac{cs}{E} \qquad (2.11)$$

The velocity c of wave propagation can be found by applying the equation of momentum. At the beginning the shaded portion of the bar was at rest, but after the lapse of the time t it has velocity v and momentum $Act\rho v$. Putting this equal to the impulse of the compressive force, we find

$$Ast = Act\rho v \qquad (2.12)$$

Using Eq. (2.11) to eliminate v in Eq. (2.12) gives

$$c = \sqrt{E/\rho} \qquad (2.13)$$

Eliminating c between Eqs. (2.11) and (2.13) gives

$$v = s/\sqrt{E\rho} \tag{2.14}$$

It will be seen that, although c is independent of the compressive force, the velocity v of particles is proportional to the stress s. Since $\sqrt{F\rho}$ is a fixed quantity for a given material, it can be seen from Eq. (2.14) that if the velocity v of the body is above a certain limit, depending on the mechanical properties of the material of the bar, a permanent set will be produced in the bar, although the mass of the striking body may be very small.

Consider now the energy of the wave shown shaded in Fig. 2.26. This energy consists of two parts: strain energy of deformation equal to

$$\text{P.E.} = \frac{Acts^2}{2E} \tag{2.15}$$

and kinetic energy equal to

$$\text{K.E.} = \frac{Act\rho v^2}{2} \tag{2.16}$$

When the value for v in Eq. (2.14) is substituted in Eq. (2.16), the kinetic energy is

$$\text{K.E.} = \frac{Acts^2}{2E}$$

It can be seen that the total energy of the wave, equal to the work done by the compressive force As acting over the distance $(s/E)ct$, is half potential and half kinetic.

It can be shown[1] that if two waves travelling in opposite directions, Fig. 2.28(a), come together, the resulting stress

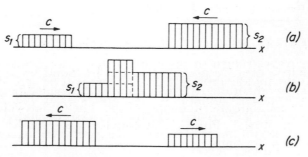

Fig. 2.28. Superposition of stress waves.

[1] S. Timoshenko and J. N. Goodier, *Theory of Elasticity*, 2nd ed. (New York: McGraw-Hill Book Co., Inc., 1951).

and the resulting velocity of particles are obtained by superposition. If both waves are, for instance, compressive waves,
the resultant compression is obtained by simple addition, as shown
in Fig. 2.28(b), and the resultant velocity of particles is obtained by
subtraction. After passing, the waves return to their initial shape,
as shown in Fig. 2.28(c).

Assume that a compression wave is moving along the bar in the x
direction and a tension wave of the same length and with the same
magnitude of stress is moving in the opposite direction, Fig. 2.29(a).
When the waves come together, tension and compression annul
each other, and in the portion of the bar in which the two waves are
superimposed we have zero stress. At the same time the velocity of
particles in this portion of the bar is doubled and equal to $2v$. After

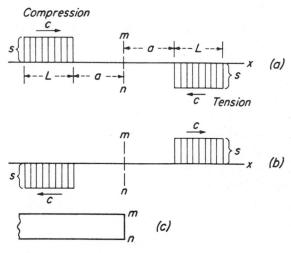

Fig. 2.29. Reflection of a stress wave from a free end.

passing, the waves return to their initial shape, as shown in Fig.
2.29(b). At the middle cross section mn there will be zero stress at
all times and we may consider it as a free end of a bar, Fig. 2.29(c).
By comparing Figs. 2.29(a) and 2.29(b), it can be concluded that in
the case of a free end, a compressive wave is reflected as a similar
tension wave, and vice versa.

If two identical waves, moving toward one another, Fig. 2.30(a),
come together, there will be doubled stress and zero particle
velocity in the portion of the bar in which the waves are superimposed. At the middle cross section mn we always have zero

particle velocity. This section remains immovable during passage of the waves and we may consider it as a fixed end of the bar, Fig. 2.30(c). Then, from comparison of Figs. 2.30(a) and (b), it can be

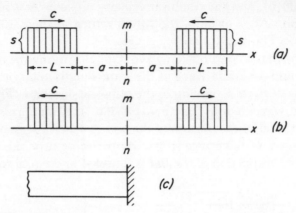

Fig. 2.30. Reflection of a stress wave from a fixed end.

concluded that a wave is reflected from a fixed end entirely un- changed.

The nature of wave reflection is also shown in Fig. 2.31 where the direction of the particle velocity is also given. At (a) the kinetic and potential energies for a length b of the compression wave are shown. At (b) the wave is being reflected from the fixed support. Here it can be seen that over the length b the strain energy is four times that of a single wave of equal length, and the kinetic energy is zero. The total energy of the superimposed waves over the length b is then twice that of a single wave. At (c) the compression wave is being reflected as a tension wave from the free end. Over the length b the energy is again double that of a single wave of the same length and is in the form of kinetic energy. At (d) the tension wave is being reflected as a tension wave.

Up to now we have considered waves produced by constant forces. The stress s and the velocity of particles v were constant along the length of the wave, but in the case of a variable force, a wave will be produced in which s and v vary along the length. Conclusions obtained before regarding propagation, superposition, and reflection of waves can be also applied in this more general case.

Consider now a more complicated problem of a bar with a fixed end struck by a moving mass at the other end, Fig. 2.32. Let M be

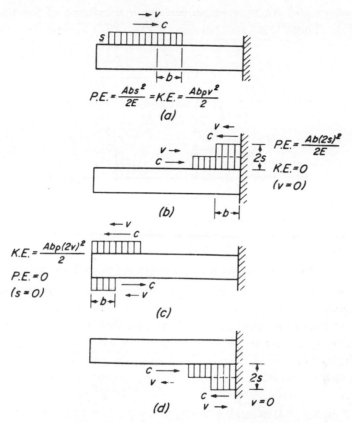

Fig. 2.31. Kinetic and potential energies in a stress wave.

the mass of the moving body per unit area of the cross section of the bar and v_0 the initial velocity of this body. Considering the body as absolutely rigid, the velocity of the particles at the end of the bar at the instant of impact ($t = 0$) is v_0, and the initial compressive stress, from Eq. (2.14), is

$$s_0 = v\sqrt{E\rho}$$

Owing to the resistance of the bar, the velocity of the moving body and hence the pressure on the bar will gradually decrease, and we obtain a compression wave with a decreasing compressive stress traveling along the length of the bar, Fig. 2.32(b). The change in compression with the time can easily be found from D'Alembert's principle. This principle states that the addition of a fictitious inertia force equal in magnitude and colinear with but opposite in

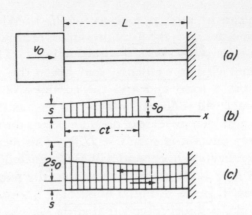

Fig. 2.32. Reflection of a stress wave from a body.

sense to the resultant of the external forces on a body, will result in a force system that is in equilibrium. That is

$$\Sigma F - ma = 0$$

Denoting by s as the variable compressive stress at the end of the bar, v as the variable velocity of the body, and noting that the resultant force per unit area acting on the striking body is $-s$, since it acts to the left when the stress is compressive (reckoned positive), we find

$$M\frac{dv}{dt} + s = 0$$

Using Eq. (2.14) to eliminate dv gives

$$\frac{M}{\sqrt{E\rho}} \cdot \frac{ds}{dt} + s = 0$$

To integrate, this equation can be put in the form

$$\int \frac{ds}{s} = -\int \frac{\sqrt{E\rho}}{M} \, dt$$

and when integrated is

$$\log s = -\frac{\sqrt{E\rho}}{M} t + C$$

When $t = 0$, $s = s_0$ which gives $C = \log s_0$. Then

$$\log s - \log s_0 = -t \frac{\sqrt{E\rho}}{M}$$

or

$$\frac{s}{s_0} = e^{-t\sqrt{E\rho}/M}, \qquad s = s_0 e^{-t\sqrt{E\rho}/M} \qquad (2.17)$$

This equation can be used so long as $t < 2L/c$. When $t = 2L/c$, the compressive wave with the front pressure s_0 returns to the end of the bar which is in contact with the moving body. The velocity of the body cannot change suddenly, and hence the wave will be reflected as from a fixed end and the compressive stress at the surface of contact will suddenly increase by $2s_0$, as shown in Fig. 2.32(c). Such a sudden increase of pressure occurs during impact at the end of every interval of time $t = 2L/c$. This theory is carried forward in the reference given, and will not be included here. The work included here is sufficient to show that the maximum stress does not necessarily occur at initial impact.

Sometimes the designer forgets that stress waves are present in all motion transfer except for the occasional case of steady state motion. It is usually assumed that the wave velocity is high in comparison with the velocity of the machine members and can be neglected, but this is not always true, as will be shown in the following example. In the gasoline engine, Fig. 2.33, the valve motion lags behind that which corresponds to the setting made when the engine was not running. The velocity of a stress wave in steel is

$$c = \sqrt{\frac{E}{\rho}} = \sqrt{\frac{30 \times 10^6 \times 32.2 \times 12}{0.28}} = 203{,}000 \text{ in. per sec}$$

or 17,000 fps, approximately.

The time required for the stress wave to travel through the valve linkage[1] of length 18.625 in., is

$$\frac{18.625}{17{,}000 \times 12} = 0.0000914 \text{ sec}$$

During this time the crankshaft turns

$$\frac{5500 \times 360 \times 0.0000914}{60} = 3.01 \text{ deg}$$

A 3 degree lag in valve motion is appreciable when it is remembered that some manufacturers specify the valve setting to a fraction of a degree.

---

[1] The wave in the rocker arm which is subjected to bending is not the same as the compression and tension waves discussed here. Since the length of the rocker arm is short in comparison with the total length of the linkage and will have little effect on the total time, it is treated as a compression wave.

When it is desired to produce plastic deformation by impact loading, the velocity of the striking mass must be great enough to

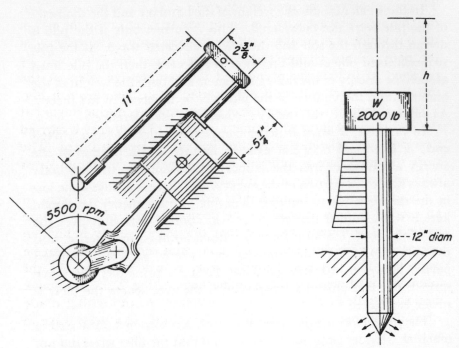

Fig. 2.33. Valve linkage of an automobile engine.

Fig. 2.34. Stress wave in a pile.

produce a stress higher than the yield. In cases where the member is not to be deformed, the velocity must be low enough to produce only stress below the yield.

In Fig. 2.34 assume that the crushing strength of the timber pile is 5500 psi, the density is 45 lb per cu ft, and the modulus of elasticity is 2,000,000 psi[1]. Determine the greatest height from which the hammer can be dropped without damaging the pile.

The maximum velocity of impact is

$$v = \frac{s}{\sqrt{E\rho}} = \frac{5500}{12\sqrt{2 \times 10^6 \times 45/1728 \times 32.2 \times 12}} = 39.5 \text{ fps}$$

The height of drop will then be

$$h = \frac{v^2}{2a} = \frac{(39.5)^2}{2 \times 32.2} = 24.3 \text{ ft}$$

---

[1] Pile driving is discussed in D. L. Thornton, *Mechanics Applied to Vibrations and Balancing*, 2nd ed. (London: Chapman & Hall, Ltd., 1951).

In these calculations the weight of the hammer and the diameter of the pile were not considered. This is correct only if the pile is driven through the soil and there is no reflected wave. If the pile strikes a fixed object and the wave is reflected, then the pile must absorb the energy of the falling hammer, and both the weight of the hammer and the volume of the pile will be involved in the theory. As indicated above, this theory is covered in the reference.

In practice, a wave is never completely reflected from a fixed end; a fixed end does not exist in nature, and a portion of the energy always goes into the support. Likewise, the striking body always absorbs a portion of the energy, and there is always some loss in the member due to internal damping. In the theory developed here it was assumed that the force was applied uniformly over the end of the bar. Uniform force is seldom attained in practice, and the failure to attain it accounts for the battered ends of hammered parts. However, because of Saint-Venant's principle, the wave spreads out and only that portion near the area where the blow is struck is affected.

The model forging hammer, Fig. 2.14, is shown in a static testing machine. Under static load it was found that the fillet stress did not increase because the portion of the base below the sow block was subjected to compression and expanded the same amount as the sow block. Under impact loading, the lateral stress wave affected the fillet region before the vertical wave reached the bottom of the base.

One of the most important concepts in this chapter is that *a rigid body does not exist in nature*. All machine members are flexible and in design this flexibility should not be ignored until consideration has shown that it is safe to do so.

Chapter 3

OPTIMUM DESIGN[1]

3.1. *Introduction*

The design of a machine usually requires many compromises. Some of the factors that must be considered are: required function, operation, reliability, safety, life, weight, service, appearance, and cost. The required function is always specified first and is, in fact, the reason why the design is undertaken. In a riveter, the required function may be the hot formation of a rivet of a certain size with a single stroke. A machine may be designed to be automatic, it may be designed for operation by a skilled operator, or it may be designed for operation by an unskilled operator. After the requirements have been met, the cost is estimated. If the cost is prohibitive, the design must be changed or some of the requirements must be relaxed. If neither choice is possible, the machine is abandoned. The optimum design is usually the design that will make the greatest profit for the company, but even this must be considered as part of the company's long-range policy. It can be seen that the balancing of the factors to obtain the optimum design is not a simple matter and requires a knowledge of the consumer's wants.

In this chapter, the efficient use of material will be considered. The efficient use of material reduces the weight to a minimum and often reduces the overall size which, in turn, reduces the costs of

---

[1] Most of the material in this chapter is based on the following sources: I. E. Morse and Ching-U Ip, "Maximum Power Transmission of Flat and V-Belts and Ropes," *Machine Design and Manufacturing Bulletin*, XII, V; W. K. Stamets, Jr., "Dynamic Loading of Chain Drives," *Trans. ASME*, **73**, 655, 1951; R. T. Hinkle, "A Simple Method of Presenting the Combined Variable-Load Equations," *Journal of Engineering Education*, March, 1951; and R. T. Hinkle, "Optimum Design," *Machine Design*, March, 1954.

materials and production. In Chapter 2, the design of an element for efficient use of material was discussed. This discussion was based on an assumed loading, but nothing was said about the control over the loading conditions that the designer sometimes has. In the case of a bolted joint, the effect of a variable load on the bolts can be changed considerably by changing the magnitude of the initial tightening of the bolts. In a power generating unit or power transmitting unit, the magnitude and nature of the loading can be altered by varying the speed. It is known that a small high speed internal combustion engine can be designed to produce the same power as a large slow speed engine. Before methods for optimum design can be developed, it will be necessary to consider the nature of varying loads and their effect on machine elements.

3.2. *Variable Loading*

A load that varies from P_{max} to P_{min} is plotted in Fig. 3.1. It has been found' that the shape of the curve has little effect on the material, and thus only the magnitudes and signs (plus or minus) of the stresses need be considered. This variable loading can be considered as a steady load, P_m (the subscript "m" stands for mean),

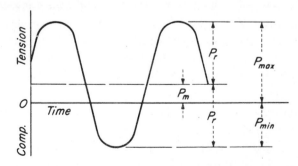

Fig. 3.1. Periodic loading.

with a superimposed reversed load, P_r. This concept may seem artificial, but it is convenient to use because the P_m component can be identified with the yield stress of the material, and the P_r component can be identified with the endurance limit.

Experimental data have been obtained from specimens subjected to various combinations of mean and reversed load components, and some of the failure points are shown in Fig. 3.2. Here the mean components are plotted as abscissae and the reversed

components are plotted as ordinates. Gerber's curve represents an
approximation of the failure points. Goodman's line is sometimes

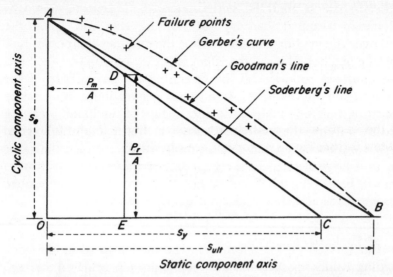

Fig. 3.2. Failure under combined static and cyclic loads.

used, but it is not consistent with the general design practice of considering the yield stress as the maximum allowable working stress.
Soderberg's line[1] is conservative and is widely used in design. Any
point on this line, such as D, will represent the limiting conditions
for design purposes.

From similar triangles ACO and DCE

$$\frac{s_y - P_m/A}{s_y} = \frac{P_r/A}{s_e} \tag{3.1}$$

This equation can be written in the form

$$s_y = \frac{P_m + P_r s_y/s_e}{A} \tag{3.2}$$

If the factor of safety is introduced and the strength-reduction
factor K_t' is applied to the variable load component, Eq. (3.2)
becomes

$$\frac{s_y}{\text{f.s.}} = \frac{P_m + K_t' P_r s_y/s_e}{A} \tag{3.3}$$

---

[1] C. R. Soderberg, "Factor of Safety and Working Stress," *Trans. ASME*,
52, 1930.

The static load equation is obtained from Eq. (3.3) by letting $P_r = 0$ and calling the static load P

$$\frac{s_y}{\text{f.s.}} = \frac{P}{A} \tag{3.4}$$

and the reversed load equation is obtained by letting $P_m = 0$

$$\frac{s_e}{\text{f.s.}} = \frac{P_r}{A} \tag{3.5}$$

If the appropriate symbols are used in Fig. 3.2, the following equations for bending and torsion are obtained

$$\frac{s_y}{\text{f.s.}} = \frac{M_m + K'_t M_r s_y / s_e}{I/c} \tag{3.6}$$

$$\frac{s_{ys}}{\text{f.s.}} = \frac{T_m + K_{ts} T_r s_y / s_e}{J/c} \tag{3.7}$$

In Eq. (3.7), s_y/s_e for tension can be used instead of the corresponding values for shear because the ratios are nearly the same.

The static and reversed load equations can be obtained from Eqs. (3.6) and (3.7) by letting the appropriate values equal zero. The static load equations are

$$\frac{s_y}{\text{f.s.}} = \frac{M}{I/c} \tag{3.8}$$

and

$$\frac{s_{ys}}{\text{f.s.}} = \frac{T}{J/c} \tag{3.9}$$

Equations (3.3) and (3.4) are identical except for the numerators of the right-hand terms, hence

$$P = P_m + \frac{K'_t s_y}{s_e} P_r \tag{3.10}$$

A reversed load P_r is more destructive than a static load of the same magnitude. The magnitude of the static load that is as destructive as the reversed load is $(K'_t s_y / s_e) P_r$. The term $(K'_t s_y / s_e)$ can be considered as a multiplying factor to increase the reversed load to an equivalent static load. This concept is important in optimum design because the variables P_m and P_r can be combined to form a single constant which depends on the yield stress of the material and the factor of safety.

In a similar manner

$$M = M_m + \frac{K'_t M_r s_y}{s_e} \tag{3.11}$$

$$T = T_m + \frac{K_{ts} T_r s_y}{s_e} \tag{3.12}$$

The equation for the section modulus of a circular shaft subjected to combined static bending and torsion is

$$\frac{\pi d^3}{16} = \frac{\sqrt{T^2 + M^2}}{s_{ys}/\text{f.s.}} \tag{3.13}$$

The "Westinghouse equation" for combined bending and torsion, both of which may be variables, can be obtained by substituting Eqs. (3.11) and (3.12) in Eq. (3.13). It is

$$\frac{\pi d^3}{16} = \frac{\sqrt{(M_m + K'_t M_r s_y/s_e)^2 + (T_m + K_{ts} T_r s_y/s_e)^2}}{s_{ys}/\text{f.s.}} \tag{3.14}$$

where　d　　= diameter of shaft
　　　　M_m　= mean component of bending moment
　　　　M_r　= reversed component of bending moment
　　　　T_m　= mean component of torsional moment
　　　　T_r　= reversed component of torsional moment
　　　　K'_t　= combined factor for bending
　　　　K_{ts}　= combined factor for torsion
　　　　s_y　= yield point in tension
　　　　s_{ys}　= yield point in shear
　　　　s_e　= endurance limit in reversed bending
　　　　f.s.　= factor of safety

3.3. *Optimum Chain Speed*

A power chain is subjected to two principal forces — power transmission and centrifugal force. As the speed approaches zero the centrifugal force approaches zero and, for constant horsepower, the power force approaches infinity. As the speed approaches infinity so does the centrifugal force, but the power force approaches zero. For a particular chain and power there is an intermediate speed at which the total stress due to static and reversed loading is at a minimum. This optimum velocity can be obtained through the use of Eq. (3.2), as follows. Centrifugal tension on a chain is constant for a given speed and equal to

$$P_c = \frac{wv^2}{32.2} \tag{3.15}$$

where w = weight of chain, lb per ft
$\quad\quad v$ = chain velocity, fps

The power force on the links is maximum on the tight side and zero on the slack side. On the tight side, the power force is

$$P_p = \frac{550 \text{ hp}}{v} \tag{3.16}$$

Form Fig. 3.3
$$P_m = P_c + \frac{P_p}{2} \tag{3.17}$$

$$P_r = \frac{P_p}{2} \tag{3.18}$$

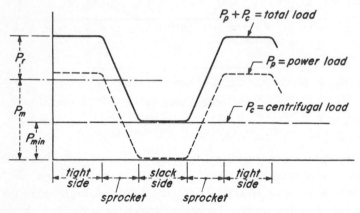

Fig. 3.3. Periodic load on chain link.

Substituting Eqs. (3.15) and (3.16) in Eq. (3.17), and Eq. (3.16) in Eq. (3.18), and then substituting these in Eq. (3.2), the total equivalent static stress becomes

$$s = \frac{1}{A}\left[\frac{wv^2}{g} + \frac{550 \text{ hp } v^{-1}}{2}\left(1 + \frac{s_y}{s_e}K\right)\right] \tag{3.19}$$

In the above equation, s, A (area), and K (stress concentration) can apply to the pins in shear, the bearing area, or to the links in tension, whichever is critical. A curve of s plotted against v has the general shape shown in Fig. 3.4. Now

$$\frac{ds}{dv} = \frac{1}{A}\left[\frac{2wv}{g} - \frac{550 \text{ hp } v^{-2}}{2}\left(1 + \frac{s_y}{s_e}K\right)\right] = 0 \tag{3.20}$$

It is evident that the second derivative would be positive, hence the value of v at which the first derivative is zero gives the minimum value of s. Solving for this optimum chain velocity

$$v_{opt} = 16.4 \sqrt[3]{\frac{\mathrm{hp}}{w}\left(1 + \frac{s_y}{s_e}K\right)} \qquad (3.21)$$

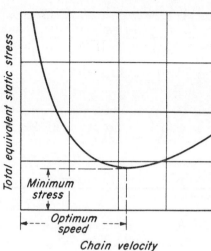

Fig. 3.4. General relationship between stress and velocity for a chain transmitting constant horsepower.

This equation was derived by Stamets[1] in a somewhat different manner. He suggests that $(1 + s_y K/s_e)$ can be taken as 5 for inverted-tooth steel chain. In many applications chains do not break but fail by wear. In some severe applications, however, chains fail by breaking.

3.4. *Optimum Belt Speed*

A belt tension formula that is commonly used is

$$\frac{F_1 - (wv^2/g)}{F_2 - (wv^2/g)} = e^{f\theta \, \mathrm{cosec} \, \alpha} \qquad (3.22)$$

where F_1 = belt tension on the tight side, lb
$\quad F_2$ = belt tension on the slack side, lb
$\quad w$ = weight of belt, lb per ft
$\quad f$ = coefficient of friction
$\quad \theta$ = angle of contact, radians
$\quad \alpha$ = half groove angle (for a flat belt, $2\alpha = 180°$ and cosec $\alpha = 1$)

---

[1] W. K. Stamets, Jr., "Dynamic Loading of Chain Drives," *Trans. ASME*, **73,** 665, 1951.

The horsepower transmitted is

$$\text{hp} = \frac{v}{550}(F_1 - F_2) \tag{3.23}$$

Eliminating F_2 from Eqs. (3.22) and (3.23) gives

$$\text{hp} = \frac{v}{550}\left(\frac{e^m - 1}{e^m}\right)\left(F_1 - \frac{wv^2}{g}\right) \tag{3.24}$$

where $m = f\theta \operatorname{cosec} \alpha$

Differentiating horsepower with respect to v and equating to zero

$$\frac{d\,(\text{hp})}{dv} = \frac{1}{550}\left(\frac{e^m - 1}{e^m}\right)\left(F_1 - \frac{3wv^2}{g}\right) = 0 \tag{3.25}$$

Since F_1 is a constant, the second derivative would be negative, hence the value of v, at which the first derivative equals zero, gives the maximum horsepower value. Solving for the optimum belt velocity

$$v = \sqrt{\frac{F_1 g}{3w}} = 3.27\sqrt{\frac{F_1}{w}} \tag{3.26}$$

or

$$\frac{wv^2}{g} = \frac{F_1}{3} \tag{3.27}$$

From Eq. (3.26), it can be seen that the optimum speed for maximum power is independent of the coefficient of friction, the angle of contact, and the groove angle. From Eq. (3.27), it can be seen that when the centrifugal force is one-third of the tight-side belt tension, maximum power is obtained.

In the preceding development, life was not considered. It is necessary to use a load that is low enough to insure long life. Rubber does not have an endurance limit; hence the number of loading cycles as well as the stress affects the life. Some life also is lost when the belt is wrapped around the large pulley even though the stress produced is less than when it is bent around the small pulley.

3.5. *Optimum Bolt Load*

An important example of optimum design technique is the determination of proper initial tightening load for bolted assemblies subjected to repeated loading. Optimum initial tightening or setting-up load is that which gives minimum equivalent static load, Eq.

(3.2), for a given external variable load.

An idealized bolted assembly is shown in Fig. 3.5. Depending on the details of the application, the assembly may or may not include gaskets at the joint faces. Presence of gaskets greatly increases the relative compliance (deformation per unit load) of the connected members in relation to that of the bolt itself.

When the bolt is tightened, and before the external load is applied, the tension load in the bolt and the compression load in the connected members are equal. Corresponding deformation of the bolt is $P_i e$ and of the connected members is $P_i c$, where P_i is the initial load, e is the elongation of the bolt per unit load (in. per lb), and c is the compression of the connected members per unit load.

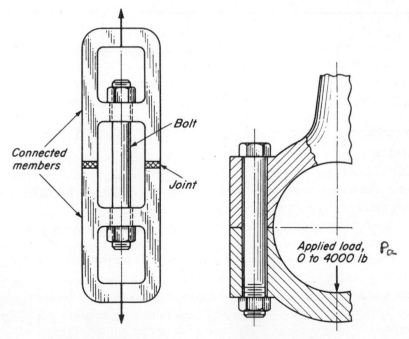

Fig. 3.5. Bolted assembly.   **Fig. 3.6.** Bolted connecting rod end.

Application of the external applied load P_a results in a final bolt load P which is generally less than $P_i + P_a$, and a final compressive load P_c in the connected members. The change in length of the bolt and connected members is equal to the final bolt length minus the initial bolt length, or $Pe - P_i e$. Final deformation of the connected members is then $P_i c - (P - P_i)e = P_c c$. Compressive load in the connected members therefore is

$$P_c = P_i - \frac{e}{c}(P - P_i) \tag{3.28}$$

Final tension in the bolt is the sum of the applied external load and the final load in the connected members,

$$P = P_c + P_a = P_i - \frac{e}{c}(P - P_i) + P_a \tag{3.29}$$

from which

$$P = \frac{c}{c + e}P_a + P_i \tag{3.30}$$

Eq. (3.30) does not hold when the joint opens, inasmuch as the connected members cannot take a tensile load. This condition requires separate investigation and will be considered later.

A connecting-rod bolt, Fig. 3.6, is a practical example of a bolted assembly which can be readily analyzed. The cylindrical portion of the rod end around the bolt, which is compressed by the tightening, may be assumed to be a hollow cylinder of uniform cross-sectional area. From the equation for elastic deformation, $\delta = PL/AE$, the unit deflection e, or stretch per unit load for the bolt is

$$e = \frac{\delta}{PL} = \frac{1}{A_b E_b} \tag{3.31}$$

and the unit compression per unit load for the hollow cylindrical portion of the connecting rod is

$$c = \frac{\delta}{PL} = \frac{1}{A_c E_c} \tag{3.32}$$

from which the factor $c/(c + e)$ in Eq. (3.30) may be written

$$\frac{c}{c + e} = \frac{A_b E_b}{A_b E_b + A_c E_c} \tag{3.33}$$

Solving for the initial tightening load from Eqs. (3.30) and (3.33)

$$P_i = P - \frac{A_b E_b}{A_b E_b + A_c E_c}P_a \tag{3.34}$$

where P_i = initial tightening load on bolt, lb
     P = final load on bolt, lb
     A_b = area of bolt shank, sq in.

P_i' ✗ = INITIAL TIGHTENING LOAD WHEN JOINT IS ON VERGE of
A_c = area of bolted member, sq in.   OPENING UNDER FULL Load
E_b = modulus of elasticity of bolt, psi P_a
E_c = modulus of elasticity of bolted member, psi
P_a = external applied load, lb

Although Eq. (3.34) applies only as long as the joint remains closed, it includes the condition when the joint is on the verge of opening, in which case the final load is equal to the external applied load, $P = P_a$. The initial load that will permit this condition is, from Eq. (3.34)

$$P_i' = \left[1 - \frac{A_b E_b}{A_b E_b + A_c E_c}\right] P_a = \frac{A_c E_c}{A_b E_b + A_c E_c} P_a \qquad (3.35)$$

where P_i' = the initial tightening load that permits the joint to be on the verge of opening when the external load, P_a, is applied to the joint. It will be shown later that P_i' is the optimum initial tightening load.

In Fig. 3.6, the externally applied load which varies from 0 to 4000 lb is divided between the two bolts. Each bolt is ½-20 NF with shank area 0.196 sq in., stress area 0.1597 sq in., and stress concentration factor $K = 2.5$. The steel of which the bolt is made has $s_y = 35,000$ psi and $s_e = 28,000$ psi. The portion of the connecting rod surrounding each steel bolt is assumed to be cylindrical with an area 1 sq in.

In this case $E_c = E_b$. Thus from Eq. (3.35), the initial tightening that will cause the joint to be on the verge of opening is

$$P_i' = \frac{1}{1 + 0.196}(2000) = 1672 \text{ lb}$$

This value is plotted in Fig. 3.7. As the load on the connecting rod varies from 0 to 4000 lb, the load on the bolt varies from 1672 to 2000 lb, while $P_m = 1836$ lb and $P_r = 164$ lb. The reversed component in terms of the equivalent static load is

$$K\frac{s_y}{s_e}P_r = (2.5)\frac{35,000}{28,000}(164) = 512 \text{ lb}$$

For this bolt a reversed loading of 164 lb is as destructive as a static load of 512 lb.

For initial tightening loads higher than 1672 lb, the final load may be determined from Eq. (3.34), which becomes

$$P = P_i + \frac{0.196}{0.196 + 1}(2000) = P_i + 328$$

The second term, 328 lb, represents twice the reversed load in the bolt. In a given application this is constant as long as the joint remains closed. Hence the final load curve is parallel to the minimum load line in this region. Tightening a bolt too much does not change the variable load component.

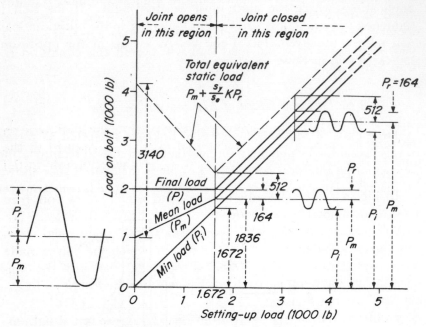

Fig. 3.7. Bolt versus setting-up load.

In the region after the joint opens the final load will always be P_a, in this example 2000 lb. If the nut is tightened just enough to be snug, the initial setting-up load is zero, $P_m = P_r = \frac{1}{2} P_a = 1000$ lb. The equivalent static load for P_r is

$$(2.5)\frac{35,000}{28,000}(1000) = 3140 \text{ lb}$$

and the total equivalent static load is $1000 + 3140 = 4140$ lb. These values are plotted in Fig. 3.7. The mean load always lies midway between the final load and the minimum load, and since the final load and minimum load curves are straight lines, the mean load and the total equivalent static load curves will also be straight lines.

It can be seen from Fig. 3.7 that the optimum setting-up load is that load which causes the joint to be on the verge of opening when the maximum external load is applied. Since all of the curves are straight lines, the entire diagram can be drawn by determining values for zero load and for optimum setting-up load.

For practical reasons the initial setting-up load on bolts is usually greater than the optimum. A large load is necessary in applications where the joint must be fluid-tight. If the bolt is tightened too much, any subsequent loosening to the optimum load will reduce the stress, but if the bolt is set up at the optimum, loosening will increase the stress.

3.6. *Optimum Speed of Mechanisms*

A large class of mechanisms involve linkages subjected to power transmission forces plus periodic inertia forces due to reciprocating or oscillating motion. A typical example is the Scotch yoke shown in Fig. 3.8. Here it is assumed that the power force is constant over

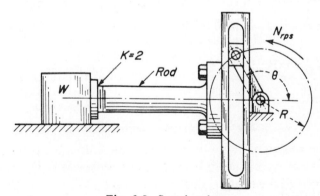

Fig. 3.8. Scotch yoke.

the first half of each cycle and zero over the remaining half. If an adequate flywheel is used the speed will be very nearly constant throughout a cycle. The loading on the horizontal rod will be investigated. The shapes of the power force and inertia force curves for this member are indicated in Fig. 3.9. The speed is $N = \omega/2\pi$ rps and during each revolution the force acts through $2R/12$ ft, where R is in inches. The power force through each half cycle is then

$$P_{\text{power}} = \frac{550 \text{ hp } (2\pi)}{\omega} \cdot \frac{12}{2R} = 20{,}800 \frac{\text{hp}}{R\omega}$$

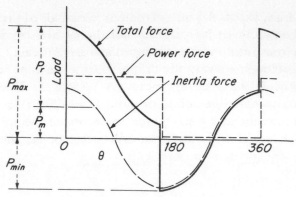

Fig. 3.9. Loading curve for Scotch yoke.

The acceleration is $(R/12)\omega^2 \cos\theta$ and the maximum inertia force is then

$$P_{\text{inertia}} = \frac{W}{32.2} \cdot \frac{R}{12}\omega^2 = 0.00258R\omega^2W$$

From Fig. 3.9 it is evident that

$$P_m = \frac{1}{2}P_{\text{power}} = \frac{10,400 \text{ hp}}{R\omega}$$

$$P_r = \frac{1}{2}(P_{\text{power}} + 2P_{\text{inertia}}) = \frac{10,400P}{R} + 0.00258R\omega^2W$$

From Eq. (3.2) the equivalent static stress is

$$s = \frac{1}{A} \cdot \frac{10,400 \text{ hp}}{R\omega} + \frac{s_y}{s_e}K \cdot \frac{10,400 \text{ hp}}{R\omega} + 0.00258R\omega^2W$$

$$= \frac{1}{A} \cdot \frac{10,400 \text{ hp}}{R\omega}\left(1 + \frac{s_y}{s_e}K\right) + 0.00258\frac{s_y}{s_e}KR\omega^2W \qquad (3.36)$$

Differentiating s with respect to ω

$$\frac{ds}{d\omega} = \frac{1}{A}\left[-\frac{10,400 \text{ hp}}{R\omega^2}\left(1 + \frac{s_y}{s_e}K\right) + 0.00516\frac{s_y}{s_e}KR\omega W\right]$$

Inasmuch as the second derivative, $d^2s/d\omega^2$, would be positive, setting $ds/d\omega$ equal to zero gives the value of ω for minimum s. When this is done

$$\omega = 126\sqrt[3]{\frac{\text{hp}}{R^2W}\left(1 + \frac{s_e}{s_yK}\right)} \qquad (3.37)$$

For a mechanism such as is shown in Fig. 3.8, with $W = 30$ lb, $R = 7$ in., hp $= 20$, material steel having $s_y = 50,000$ psi and $s_e = 30,000$ psi, the stress-concentration factor at thread $K = 2$, the value of ω from Eq. (3.37) is 32.8 radians per sec or 314 rpm. If the rod is threaded ¾-10 NC, the cross-sectional area at the thread roots is 0.3 sq in., and the stress at optimum speed is, from Eq. (3.36) 19,500 psi. How stress varies with speed (for a constant hp = 20) is shown in Fig. 3.10.

For an alternative design with the crank radius reduced to 3.5 in. and the weight to 7.5 lb, the optimum speed from Eq. (3.37), becomes 785 rpm. For the same stress, 19,500 psi, the rod area

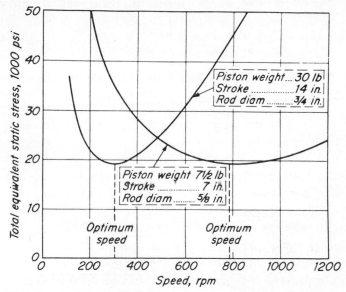

Fig. 3.10. Total equivalent static stresses for two mechanisms of different size, both transmitting the same power.

could be reduced to 0.238 sq in., or a ⅝-NF thread. These changes thus result in a smaller and lighter machine with higher optimum speed for the same power capacity, as is shown in Fig. 3.10. Whether such changes are feasible depends on the nature of the problem.

3.7. *Speed and Size Relationships*

The foregoing example, and Fig. 3.10, demonstrate that optimum speed increases as the size of a machine or mechanism decreases. With optimum speed established for a particular configuration and stress condition, it is possible with the aid of Eq. (3.37) to set up a relationship between speed, size, power capacity, etc., for an entire line of geometrically similar machines.

The size of the machine or mechanism is denoted by some basic dimension d which could be a cylinder bore, a shaft diameter or some other convenient measurement. Then all weights such as W in Eq. (3.37) are proportional to d^3, linear dimensions such as R are proportional to d, and horsepower capacity is proportional to $d^3\omega$. The last relation is easily derived: power equals force times linear velocity, but force equals stress times area; therefore, for the same stresses, power forces are proportional to area and therefore to d^2. Linear velocity is also proportional to linear dimension times angular velocity and is therefore proportional to $d\omega$. Substituting in Eq. (3.37) the foregoing relationships, i.e., $W \propto d^3$, $R \propto d$, and hp $\propto d^3\omega$

$$\omega \propto \sqrt[3]{\frac{d^3\omega}{d^2 d^3}} \quad \text{or} \quad \omega \propto \frac{1}{d} \tag{3.38}$$

Because all stress relationships are identical, they can be treated as constants.

The fact that optimum speed is inversely proportional to size leads to some interesting conclusions. While weight is proportional to the cube of dimensions, power capacity is proportional only to the square of linear dimensions; hence weight per horsepower increases in linear proportion to size. This fact should be remembered in comparing performances of large and small engines, pumps, or compressors, to mention only a few typical machines.

As an example, it is conceivable that an automobile engine delivering 150 hp at 3600 rpm and weighing 750 lb could be built to identical proportions in larger or smaller sizes. If it were built twice as large it would have to run at only 1800 rpm for the same stresses but it would deliver 600 hp. However, it would weigh 6000 lb, and would deliver only half as much horsepower per pound of weight as the smaller engine. The basic reason for this fact is very simple. If each unit volume of material in the two engines is thought of as a tool for doing work, a unit volume in the high speed engine will do twice as much work as a unit volume in the slow speed engine because it is used twice as often.

3.8. *Optimum Design of Machines*

In Arts. 3.3 through 3.6, the optimum design of individual machine elements was considered. If an optimum speed for several members is to be obtained in this manner and the members are made of materials having different yield points, then it is necessary to adjust the curves to one yield point. An example is shown in Fig. 3.11. Stress-speed curves are plotted for two members, 1 and 2,

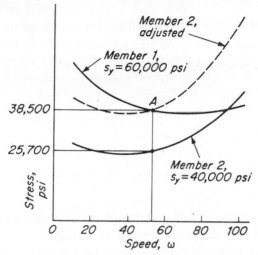

Fig. 3.11. Stresses in two machine members of different material compared by adjusting for different yield strengths.

having yield points of 60,000 and 40,000 psi, respectively. The curve for member 2 is increased by the factor 60,000/40,000. The optimum speed is given by the intersection A, the lowest point common to both members. For this speed the factor of safety for both members is

$$\frac{60,000}{38,000} = \frac{40,000}{25,700} = 1.56$$

Any number of curves can be adjusted to a chosen stress in this manner.

The ideal machine is often considered to be one in which the factors of safety for all members are equal. The adjusted stress-speed curves for the members of such a machine appear in Fig. 3.12. Here the machine was designed to operate at speed ω_1. Any speed between ω_1 and ω_3 would reduce the stresses and the optimum would be ω_2.

The determination of the optimum speed of the crankshaft, Fig. 3.8, is tedious[1]. If it is assumed that the maximum bending

---

[1] R. T. Hinkle, "Optimum Design," *Machine Design*, March, 1954.

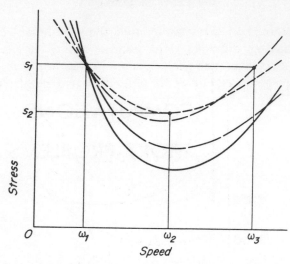

Fig. 3.12. Stress-speed curves for four different members in the same machine.

moment and torque occur simultaneously (an assumption which is on the side of safety), the analysis is simplified.

After a machine has been designed, curves similar to those shown in Fig. 3.12 can be obtained by assuming a series of speeds and calculating the stresses in the members. After a machine of a chosen size and speed has been designed, other sizes that are geometrically similar can be easily investigated by use of Eq. (3.38).

The method described in this chapter should not be considered as a universal method for all designs, but it can be considered as an additional tool that in some cases can be used for making better designs.

Chapter 4

COMPUTATIONS

SHORT PROBLEMS

4.1. *Form of Computations*

It is important that design computations be made in an orderly manner. There are two reasons for this: first, the designer can work more efficiently and will make fewer errors; second, the computations become the property of the company and must be used by others. It is necessary that engineers be able to follow the computations without frequent consultation with the designer to clear up points that were not adequately explained or labeled. If the machine proves to be unsatisfactory in the experimental laboratory or in the field, the computations may be checked again. They will usually be referred to if the machine is redesigned or if a similar machine is designed.

The following items can be used as a guide by students. In general they can be used in industry.

(1) *Read the problem.* The entire problem should be read and understood before work is started. Sometimes the instructions given with an examination are "Do not begin writing for thirty minutes." Not only should the problem be read and understood but a general method of attack for completing the entire problem should be determined before numerical work is begun.

(2) Each sheet should carry the student's name, the date, and consecutive numbers if more than one sheet is used. Such identifications are essential and may be of importance if the question of patents arises.

(3) Only one side of the paper should be used and a margin

of one inch should be included on all sides. Some companies have their own standard paper with headings and blanks to be filled in. In some cases vellum is used so that prints can be made.

(4) If possible, a sketch should be drawn for every problem. The sketch should be neat and correct and should show the arrangement of parts and such data as dimensions, speeds, etc. For data that cannot be shown on the sketch, a list should be used. A sketch with data helps to clarify the problem. It is more convenient to use the sketch as a source for data than to use a written description. Frequent reference to the sketch while calculations are being made helps to prevent errors.

(5) Each step in the solution should be set off, labeled, or lettered so that divisions can be readily identified.

(6) Sources of information should be given, although the sources of commonly used equations and other information do not have to be given. However, the sources of less commonly used equations and information should be given by listing the publication and page. If a particular manufacturer's product is to be incorporated in the machine, this fact should be stated.

(7) If equations are used, the equations should be solved for the desired quantity *before* numerical substitutions are made. In many cases the final result is not satisfactory, and thus it is necessary to go back and change some of the data. Writing the equation in this form facilitates the work, for if the equation is not written in this form, the designer must transpose the numbers mentally while he is performing slide rule operations.

(8) The numerical substitution should follow directly below the equation and the terms should follow the literal equation in order. This makes the work of checking easier and also helps the student if he must go back over his work to look for errors or to make changes. Each numerical value can be identified by looking at the corresponding symbol in the equation.

(9) Units should not be placed in numerical equations. If a check on units is necessary, a separate dimensional equation should be used. The determination of a numerical value and a dimensional check are two separate operations. The combination of these operations in a long equation is confusing and may lead to errors.

(10) Units should be indicated for every separate value that has units, whether it be data, intermediate calculated value, or final value.

(11) Long equations should be avoided. Instead, intermediate values, particularly physical quantities, should be determined

separately before insertion into the longer equation.

(12) Care should be exercised to obtain the greatest accuracy that the slide rule will permit, but an unjustified number of significant figures should not be used.

(13) Whenever applicable, calculated dimensions should be rounded out to nominal sizes, and indicated: For example, $d =$ 1.94, "Use 2 in." Do not round out intermediate values. Whenever possible, stock items with the least amount of alteration should be used.

(14) Values in an equation in formal computations should not be cancelled, although this can be done on scratch paper if desired. The drawing of a line through a number is reserved for changes. If the final value is not satisfactory, some of the data must be changed. The data can be changed by drawing a line through the value that is to be changed and all following values that are affected by this change. The new value is written above or below the old value and the necessary calculations are repeated. It may be necessary to do this several times. In some cases the designer will want to erase the old value and include only the new, but in others he will want to leave all values to show why certain changes were necessary.

(15) All results should be tested for probability. Most of the absurd results that a student may submit could be avoided if he would consider each one. In some cases an experienced engineer can recognize that his result is incorrect if it is off more than ten or fifteen percent, although the student may not be able to recognize an error that is less than two or three hundred percent. The important thing is to form the habit of testing for probability. Accuracy will come with experience.

It should be remembered that the difference between the outstanding man and the mediocre man is often marginal. The young engineer who has developed neat, orderly habits is more likely to make a favorable impression on his superiors and co-workers. Although there is no substitute for technical knowledge, it alone is not sufficient to insure success.

4.2. *Short Problems in Design*

Problem 4.1

(a) For the tumbling barrel shown in Fig. P4.1, determine the limiting speed for tumbling action.

(b) Determine the maximum horsepower that is required to operate the barrel for the following conditions: maximum weight of material to be tumbled, 240 lb per cu ft; efficiency of drive, 85%; speed, 75% of limiting speed determined in part (a).

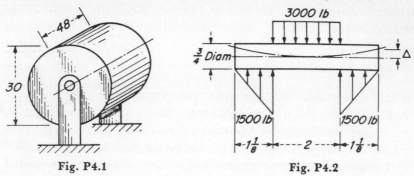

Fig. P4.1   Fig. P4.2

(c) For a speed of 30 rpm, locate the point on the inside surface of the barrel where a particle will leave contact, and the point where it will again strike the surface. Assume that friction prevents the particle from sliding on the surface.

Problem 4.2

Determine the deflection Δ for the steel pin shown in Fig. P4.2.

Problem 4.3

In the pin connection, Fig. P4.3(a), the clearance has been exaggerated to help in visualizing the deflection. This type of

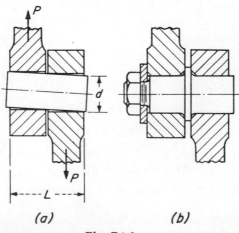

(a)   (b)

Fig. P4.3

connection is inexpensive but it does not represent good design for many applications, especially from the standpoint of wear. The type shown at (b) is better.

For the type shown at (a), assume a reasonable load distribution and determine the L/d ratio so that the pin is equally strong in shear and bending.

Problem 4.4

The spring shown in Fig. P4.4 is made of Fiberglas having the following properties: $s_{\text{ult}} = 100{,}000$ psi, $E = 4{,}000{,}000$ psi.

(a) Using only the equations $\delta = PL^3/3EI$ and $s = Mc/I$, determine the factor of safety based on the ultimate strength.

(b) Determine the factor of safety assuming that the material is steel having an ultimate strength of 100,000 psi and E of 30,000,000 psi.

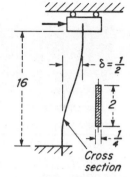

Fig. P4.4

Problem 4.5

An overload unit is to be incorporated in the coupler link of the four bar linkage shown in Fig. P4.5. The unit is to act as a rigid body until a force of 150 lb is applied. Then it must be capable of operating when the coupler link is subjected to either tension or

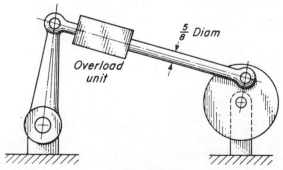

Fig. P4.5

compression, and must absorb 200 lb-in. of energy without exceeding a force of 400 lb. One coil spring is to be used. Design a suitable unit and describe it in a neat, freehand sketch.

Problem 4.6

A bumper utilizing a single coil spring is to be designed to absorb elastically 60 lb-ft of energy. Since only one bumper is to be made and a variety of springs are on hand, it is desired to use one of these springs. The wire diameters of most of the springs fall in the $\frac{3}{8}$ to $\frac{5}{8}$ in. range. The application is severe. Determine the approximate minimum weight of the spring that will serve the purpose. This weight value can be used to eliminate many of the springs in the group.

Problem 4.7

The designer is usually not responsible for failure of a machine due to abuse, although in some cases he can design a machine to prevent extensive damage by considering possible abuse. In a hand-operated arbor press, the handle can be designed to bend before any other parts fail. The resistance to bending increases as plastic bending progresses, and a workman could increase the applied load beyond that of the maximum elastic bending of the handle. For a round bar, determine the ratio of maximum plastic moment to the elastic moment. Assume an idealized stress-strain curve.

Problem 4.8

The shearing stress at any point in an eccentrically loaded welded joint is usually determined from the following equation

$$s_s = \frac{P}{A} \longmapsto \frac{Per}{J}$$

where A is the area of the throat of the welds and J is the polar moment of inertia of the area about its center of gravity (see Fig. P4.8).

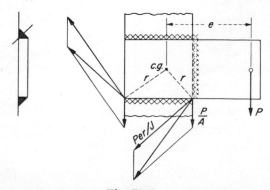

Fig. P4.8

In many text books it is stated that the equation $s_s = Tc/J$ applies only to a solid circular bar or a circular bar with a concentric hole. It can be shown that for a rectangular bar in torsion, the stress is zero at the corners of a cross-section and a maximum at the center of a long side. Explain why the above equation for a welded joint is approximately correct.

Problem 4.9

From the theory of mechanics and rigid bodies, it is known that a toggle linkage can ideally produce an infinite force. When an actual machine that is made of elastic materials having ultimate strengths is considered, the force that can be produced is limited by the strength of the parts. In most cases it is desirable that the yield stress not be exceeded.

The riveter, Fig. P4.9, employs a simple toggle linkage to produce an increasing force to overcome the increasing resistance of the rivet as the head is formed. If the riveter is properly adjusted, and the work to be performed does not exceed the rated value, the

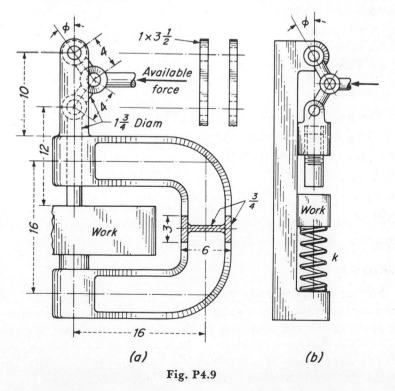

(a)　　　　　　　　　　　　　(b)

Fig. P4.9

riveter will not be damaged. In a general-purpose machine of this type it is probable that at some time it will be improperly used, and it is therefore desirable to design it so that improper use will not cause damage. The riveter can be most easily investigated by considering the equivalent system shown at (b) where the flexibility of the members has been reduced to a single spring with constant k. If the maximum allowable load on the spring is taken as the load corresponding to the yield of the riveter under rated load, and if it is assumed that the work does not deform, the system can be investigated for different adjustments and the available force thereby limited so that no damage can be done. In some cases a fairly accurate determination of the spring constant for the system can be made analytically, while in others, due to complex parts, it is necessary to determine it experimentally.

In this problem, determine the spring constant k. The material is steel with a yield stress of 60,000 psi. Neglect stress concentration, curvature, and shear deflection. Work from the center lines and assume that the angles of intersection remain unchanged when load is applied. Assuming that the work does not deform, determine the maximum angle ϕ for the toggle links, so that, if a force is applied which brings the links into the colinear position, the yield stress in the frame is not exceeded.

Problem 4.10

The front wheels of the lift truck, Fig. P4.10, are made of steel and are 2 in. in diameter. A $\frac{1}{32}$ in. steel plate has been placed in front of the wheels as shown.

(a) Neglecting friction, determine in pounds the push required to move the truck forward.

(b) Determine the diameter of the front wheels which will permit forward motion when a push of 100 lb is applied. All other conditions are the same as stated above.

Problem 4.11

For an eye bar of the proportions shown[1] in Fig. P4.11, the stress concentration factor at the hole is 2.8. Determine the ratio of the stress in the eye and that in the shank. Show that, for most

---

[1] Frost and Richards, "Eye-Bolt Stresses as Determined by Photoelastic Test," *Journal of the Society of Automotive Engineers*, **XVII**, August, 1925, p. 213.

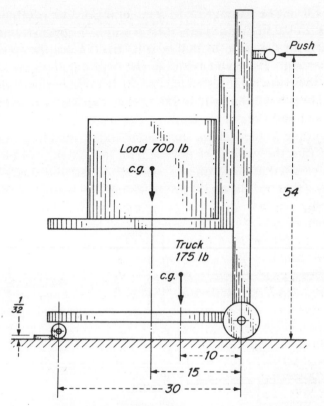

Fig. P4.10

applications, the strength ratio of the eye and shank is more favorable than this. Assume reasonable numerical values and determine the numerical ratio.

Problem 4.12

A steel torque rod and arm are shown in Fig. P4.12.

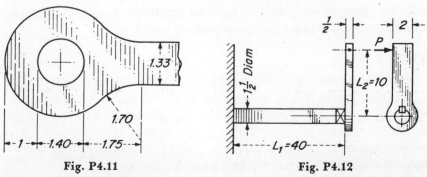

Fig. P4.11   **Fig. P4.12**

(a) For a maximum direct stress of 60,000 psi, determine the energy in in.-lb that the system can absorb. Neglect stress concentration and bending in the rod which results from the force P not passing through the center plane of the bearing.

(b) Same as part (a), except that the bearing has been removed.

(c) Determine the ratio of the energy capacities as determined in parts (a) and (b).

Problem 4.13

The torque wrench, Fig. P4.13, has a maximum capacity of 300 lb-ft. For this torque, the deflection on the scale is to be $3\frac{3}{8}$ in.

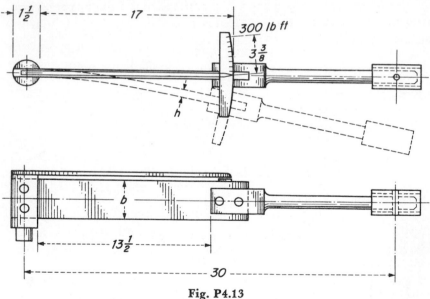

Fig. P4.13

as shown in the figure (the chord and arc lengths are nearly equal) and the stress in the steel deflection member is not to exceed 125,000 psi. Determine the dimensions h and b.

Problem 4.14

A vibrating conveyor, Fig. P4.14, has a stroke of 1 in., frequency of 470 cpm, and an axis of bed motion of 30 deg with the horizontal. The bed moves with simple harmonic motion. Determine the theoretical speed of conveying. The theoretical speed is the average speed at which a particle would be conveyed if there were no slipping between the bed and the particles.

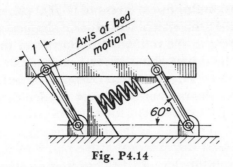

Fig. P4.14

Problem 4.15

For a bolt that is subjected to a repeated load that varies from zero to a maximum, the maximum strain energy for an infinite number of cycles is given by the equation

$$\text{strain energy} = \frac{2L}{A_\Delta E}\left(\frac{s_y A_s}{1 + (Ks_y/s_e)}\right)^2$$

where s_y = yield stress
  s_e = endurance limit
  K = fatigue stress concentration factor
  L = length of shank
  A_Δ = area of shank
  A_s = area of section where stress is a maximum

Derive the above equation.

(a) The bolt shown in Fig. P4.15(a) is subjected to a repeated

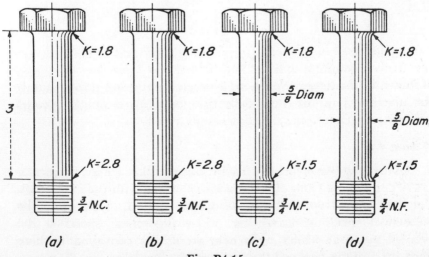

Fig. P4.15

load (varies from zero to a maximum). The ultimate and yield stresses for the material are 67,000 and 45,000 psi, respectively, and the bolt is machined. Determine the strain energy per cycle for an infinite number of cycles that the bolt is capable of absorbing.

(b) Same as part (a), except that the bolt shown at (b) is to be considered. The material and finish are the same as for bolt (a).

(c) Same as part (a), except that the bolt shown at (c) is to be considered. The material and finish are the same as for bolt (a).

(d) Same as part (a), except that the bolt shown at (d) is to be considered. The ultimate and yield stresses for the material are 150,000 and 135,000 psi, respectively, and the bolt is polished.

Problem 4.16

A machine utilizes torque that varies from 1200 to 2100 lb-in. during each cycle. This torque is supplied from a driving sprocket which is mounted as shown in Fig. P4.16. The shaft is made of steel

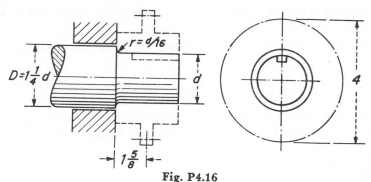

Fig. P4.16

having ultimate and yield stresses of 95,000 and 52,000 psi, respectively. Assuming that the shaft is machined and that the factor of safety is 2.5, determine the dimensions d, D, and r. The speed of the machine is approximately 45% of the speed of the driving sprocket.

Problem 4.17

The maximum speed of the 4-cycle gasoline engine shown in Fig. P4.17 is 4600 rpm. The weight of the piston and pin is 1.75 lb, and the weight of the rod, excluding the cap, is 1.61 lb. The bolts are made of steel having ultimate and yield stresses of 190,000 and 158,000 psi, respectively. The portion of the rod through which each bolt passes is an approximate cylinder ⅝ in. in diameter.

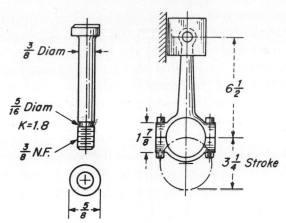

Fig. P4.17

The stress concentration factor includes both the geometric and surface factors.

(a) Determine the optimum setting-up load for the bolts.

(b) Determine the factor of safety when the setting-up load is optimum.

(c) Determine the factor of safety when the setting-up load is 150% of the optimum.

(d) Determine the factor of safety when the setting-up load is zero.

(e) Determine the percentage of overload tightening that will produce the same factor of safety as zero setting-up load.

Problem 4.18

For the mechanism shown in Fig. 3.8, assume that $W = 3.75$ lb, hp $= 5$, $R = 3.5$ in., speed $= 628$ rpm, and the material and stress concentration factor are the same as in the example. Using Eq. 3.36 and an induced equivalent static stress of 19,500 psi, determine the required area of the rod. Check to determine if the diameter of the rod is one half that of the rod in the example, Art. 3.6.

Problem 4.19

This problem can be used by the reader to check his capacity for basic thinking. A steel rod 17,000 ft long is suspended as shown. According to theory, if the top end is instantly cut, the bottom end will not receive this information for one second and will not begin to fall until it has received the signal that it is no longer supported. Explain what takes place.

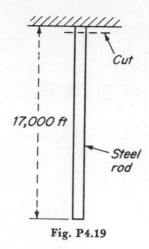

Fig. P4.19

Problem 4.20

In Fig. P4.20, a pressure of 60,000 psi is applied to the top area of the steel sow block. Assuming that the base does not deform, determine the force that tends to spread the base. Determine the dimensions of the sow block after the pressure has been applied.

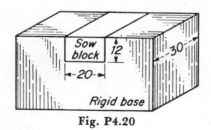

Fig. P4.20

Chapter 5

CENTRIFUGAL
COUPLING

5.1. *Introduction*

The type of centrifugal coupling described here can be used to fulfill the three following functions: to accommodate slight misalignment of the shafts, to limit the starting load on the power source, and to act as a slip coupling in case of an excessive overload.

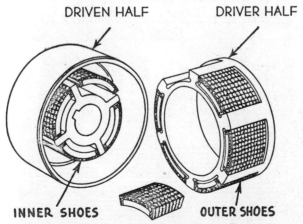

Fig. 5.1. Rawson centrifugal coupling.
[Courtesy O. S. Walker Co., Inc.]

The parts of a Rawson coupling are shown in Fig. 5.1. The manner in which a machine is driven by an electric motor through this coupling is as follows. The driving half, which is attached to the motor, attains full speed soon after the motor has been started. By means of lead weights the mass of the outer shoes is adjusted so that, at full speed, the friction torque on the driven half is equal to the rated torque of the motor. As the driven half comes up to full speed, the inner shoes produce a frictional torque on the driving half. The time required to bring a machine up to speed depends on the work performed by the machine and its inertia. The weight of the inner shoes is adjusted to give the desired full speed overload capacity. The entire capacity could be put into the outer shoes but the use of two sets of shoes produces smoother starting and reduces the starting current to the motor.

In the application, Fig. 5.2, the coupling is incorporated in a V-belt drive.

Fig. 5.2. A 15-hp, 1750-rpm, squirrel-cage motor driving a compressor through a Rawson coupling. [Courtesy O. S. Walker Co., Inc.]

5.2. *Problem*

The general requirements are: a 30 hp induction motor is to be coupled to a coal pulverizer by means of a Rawson centrifugal coupling.

The specifications and design data are:

1. *Pulverizer:* The inertia load is $WR^2 = 3415$ lb-ft². The power requirements have been determined experimentally to average 30 hp, but due to chunks of coal, there may be 75 per cent overloads of short duration.

2. *Squirrel-cage induction motor:* 30 hp, 230 volt, 60 cycle, 3 phase, 1150 rpm full load speed. Since the overloads are of short duration, the speed is assumed to be constant.

3. *Coupling:* The coefficient of friction for brake lining and cast iron is 0.34. The center of gravity of the lead weighted shoes is located approximately ⅜ in. inward from the friction surface.

(a) Select the coupling size from Table 5.1.

TABLE 5.1

MAXIMUM NORMAL CAPACITY OF RAWSON COUPLING*

Coupling size	Outer drum	Inner drum	390 rpm	490 rpm	580 rpm	690 rpm	725 rpm	870 rpm	1150 rpm	1450 rpm	1750 rpm	2500 rpm	3450 rpm	3600 rpm
	I.D., in.		Maximum Normal Capacity (horsepower)											
3½ × 1½	3½	..	.04	.08	.13	.2	.23	.4	1.0	2.1	3.6	9.2	11.5	12
4 × 1½	4	..	.06	.12	.20	.3	.35	.6	1.5	3.1	5.3	10.5	14.0	15
5 × 1½	5	3½	.09	.16	.27	.4	.46	.8	2.1	4.3	7.5	15.5	22.0	..
6 × 2	6	4	.28	.5	.9	1.3	1.6	2.7	6.8	14.0	19.0	31.0	..	..
7 × 2½	7	5	.6	1.1	1.9	2.8	3.2	5.9	15.0	30.0	35.0	..	..	..
8 × 3	8	5½	1.0	2.0	3.4	5.0	5.8	10.0	25.0	47.0	60.0	..	..	..
10 × 3	10	7	3.8	7.4	12.0	18.0	21.0	40.0	60.0	75.0	90.0	..	..	..
12 × 4	12	8¾	10.0	19.0	32.0	48.0	56.0	83.0	110.0	140.0	160.0	..	..	..
14 × 4	14	10	20.0	38.0	64.0	85.0	90.0	110.0	150.0	180.0	..	..	..	..
16 × 5	16	12	38.0	72.0	120.0	150.0	160.0	200.0	250.0	..	..	..	..	..
19 × 5	19	14	95.0	160.0	200.0	220.0	240.0	290.0	..	..	..	..	..	..
21 × 6	21	16	150.0	240.0	290.0	330.0	350.0	425.0	..	..	..	..	..	..
24 × 8	24	19	250.0	400.0	475.0	550.0	..	..	..	..	..	..	..	..

* Maximum normal capacity is that rated horsepower which the Rawson Coupling can carry without the shoe pressure exceeding 25 psi — the maximum allowable for long shoe life.

(b) The outer shoes are to provide capacity for 100 per cent of motor torque rating and the inner shoes are to provide 75 per cent overload capacity. Assuming six shoes per set, determine the proper shoe weights in ounces for both outer and inner sets.

(c) Using the calculus, determine the acceleration time with the above shoe weights. Assume that the motor acceleration time is negligible compared with the total time involved, giving constant torque for the outer shoes and variable torque for the inner shoes.

(d)   Determine the acceleration time using the approximation that the inner shoes exert a constant torque equal to $\frac{1}{4}$ the final torque.

(e)   Using the approximate method indicated in part (d), select new shoe weights to give an acceleration time of 60 sec. The total capacity of 175 per cent is to be maintained.

(f)   Determine the minimum possible acceleration time with 175 per cent of motor rating that can be obtained with this coupling.

Chapter 6

NATURAL FREQUENCY

OSCILLATING

CONVEYOR

6.1. *Introduction*

The illustrations that follow show several models of natural frequency conveyors. The parts of the conveyor are shown in Fig. 6.1, and the manner in which the material is conveyed is shown in Fig. 6.2. The bed is caused to vibrate along the axis of the coil springs by means of a positive stroke drive. The motion of a conveyed particle is shown in Fig. 6.2(b), the sine curve represents the vertical displacement of the conveyor bed plotted against time. The particle is carried on the bed to a point A on the up-stroke where it is thrown free. The particle then travels through space until it is caught on the bed near the bottom of its stroke, point B, and is then carried forward and upward on the bed to C where it is thrown free, etc.

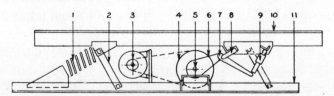

Fig. 6.1. Parts of a natural frequency vibrating conveyor: 1, coil spring; 2, stabilizer leaf springs; 3, motor; 4, sheave; 5, eccentric shaft; 6, drive arm; 7, lever arm; 8, pivot link; 9, shock absorber; 10, trough; 11, base. [Courtesy Carrier Conveyor Corp.]

Conveyors that are driven by an unbalanced rotating weight, Fig. 6.3(a), have the motion characteristics shown at (b). If the unit is operated with a constant source of energy near the natural

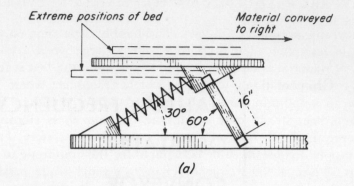

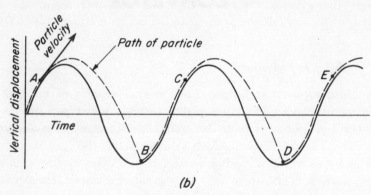

Fig. 6.2. Path of particle during conveying.

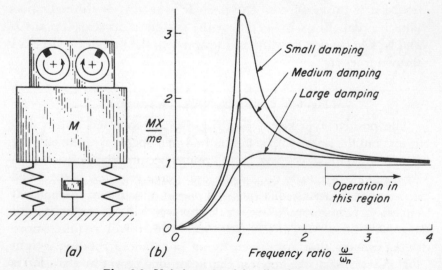

Fig. 6.3. Unbalanced weight vibrating system.

frequency, the amplitude will vary considerably depending on the amount of damping. The amplitude will be large when a small amount of material is on the bed and small when the bed is full. For this reason operation is usually at a higher frequency where the variation in amplitude due to change in damping is slight. The curves represent steady state conditions. A large mass vibrating with a large amplitude has considerable energy, and therefore, if the energy supply is constant, time is required for the amplitude to be built up. Thus, if the frequency changes rapidly while passing through the critical region, while starting and stopping, the amplitude does not have time to build up to a dangerous value.

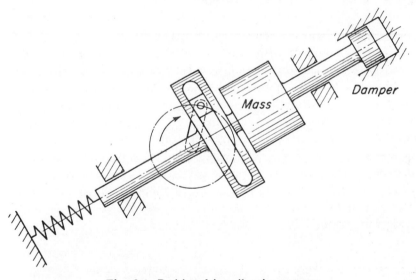

Fig. 6.4. Positive drive vibrating system.

The positive type drive, Fig. 6.4, can be operated at any frequency, but the forces will be minimum when operated at the natural frequency. The forces will be minimum because the unit tends to vibrate at this frequency, and the only force required is the force necessary to overcome damping. If operation is not at the natural frequency, stronger members and bearings will be required and there will be greater frictional losses which will require more driving power.

If the type of drive shown in Fig. 6.3 is used[1] and the operation is

---

[1] See W. T. Thomson, *Mechanical Vibrations,* 2nd ed. (Englewood Cliffs, N. J.: Prentice-Hall, Inc., 1953) p. 74.

near the natural frequency, the impressed force is in phase with the velocity and all of the energy that the motor is capable of supplying is used to build up a large amplitude. The amplitude is limited only when the energy of damping (this includes the energy required to throw the particles) is equal to the maximum energy that the motor is capable of supplying. In Fig. 6.4, the amplitude of vibration is constant and the energy is supplied in a different manner. After the natural frequency is reached, energy is supplied by the crank pushing against the side of the slot when the amplitude of the vibrating mass tends to decrease due to damping. The only energy that is supplied is that necessary to keep the amplitude up to the predetermined value — the stroke of the crank. If there were no damping, the mass would vibrate and the block on the crank would oscillate, relative to the slot, without pressing against the sides. There would be no energy input. The conveyors shown in the accompanying illustrations operate on this principle.

Vibrating conveyors are not suitable for all materials, e.g., fine material such as flour or cement dust tends to aerate. Sticky or semi-liquid materials cannot always be handled successfully. However, most materials can be conveyed in this manner, and often conveying can be combined with other processes. In Fig. 6.5, sand and castings are separated during conveying. Materials with temperatures as high as 1800 degrees Fahrenheit can be conveyed and cooled. Slag and low melting-point salts can be cooled and, due to vibration, can be fractured as hardening takes place. Material can be totally enclosed by the use of dust covers with flexible hose connections at inlet and outlet.

6.2. *Specifications for Natural-Frequency Positive-Drive Conveyor*

The conveyor is to carry 120 tons of damp sand per hour, horizontally, a distance of 40 ft. Damp sand weighs 100 lb per cu ft. The frequency is to be 470 cpm and the stroke 1 in. The conveyor is to be made in 10 ft sections welded together during installation. It is desirable to place the driving unit near the center of the conveyor. The overall factor of safety should be approximately 3, and the bearing life is to be 10,000 hours.

Assume that the conveying speed is 90 fpm. This speed has been determined experimentally and is greater than the theoretical

Fig. 6.5. This 30-ft conveyor is located in a brass foundry and handles 160 tons of sand and hot castings per hour. The last 20 ft (at left) is double-decked, the top deck being a grating to separate the sand from the castings. The bottom deck carries the sand to the end of the conveyor, where it is discharged into a bucket elevator and returned to the sand system. [Courtesy Carrier Conveyor Corp.]

Fig. 6.6. Driving unit for conveyor in Fig. 6.5. A 5-hp motor is used. [Courtesy Carrier Conveyor Corp.]

Fig. 6.7. Conveyor to handle and cool red-hot material. Note ⅝-in. thick pan and spring-loaded hold-down bolts in slots to allow for expansion and contraction. The space between the top and bottom decks allows room for water spray pipes. The bottom pan catches excess water and drains it off. [Courtesy Carrier Conveyor Corp.]

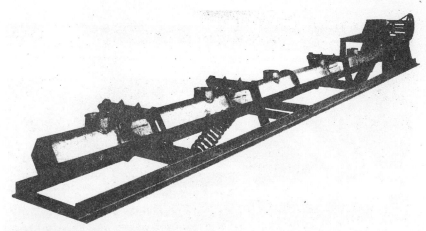

Fig. 6.8. A specially designed 10-in. hexagonal tube, 26-ft long conveyor for detergent powders. A ½-hp motor is used. [Courtesy Carrier Conveyor Corp.]

speed, the theoretical speed being the speed that the sand would have if there were no slipping on the bed. Investigations with a stroboscope indicate that the sand slides forward on the bed before leaving contact and after recontact. The sand leaves contact with the bed when the downward acceleration of the bed is 1.0g. During the downward acceleration of the bed the horizontal velocity is decreasing. Before the acceleration of 1.0g is reached the force between the bed and sand is reduced sufficiently so that the sand slides forward on the bed and leaves contact with a greater horizontal velocity than the horizontal velocity of the bed. Recontact is made when the bed is near its lowest position, and the velocity of

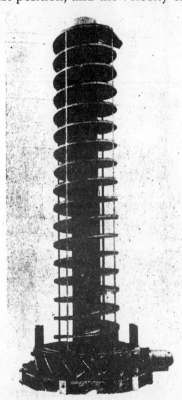

Fig. 6.9. A spiral conveyor, 18 ft high, for elevating and cooling pelletized fertilizer. Note holes for air cooling, just above flights. The air connection is at the top of the center tube, which acts as a plenum chamber. The elevation rate is 5 fpm. A ¾-hp motor is used. [Courtesy Carrier Conveyor Corp.]

the bed is small. The sand slides forward due to the horizontal component of its velocity. Some materials have considerable particle slipping. Corn, for example, conveys at approximately 55% of theoretical speed. It has been found that the natural frequency of this type of conveyor, when loaded, is very nearly the same as the empty conveyor providing the weight of the bed equals

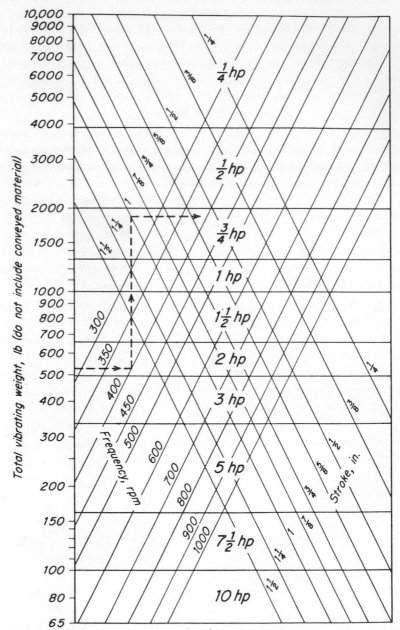

Fig. 6.10. Starting horsepower chart. To use, (1) locate the total vibrating weight (bed and material to be conveyed) at the left of the chart, (2) proceed horizontally to diagonal line indicating frequency, (3) proceed vertically to diagonal stroke line, (4) read hp between horizontal divisions. [Courtesy Carrier Conveyor Corp.]

or exceeds the weight of the conveyed material. Damp sand can be conveyed satisfactorily when 4 in. deep with bed sides 6 in. high.

The horsepower of the motor must be sufficient for both starting and operation at normal speed. The starting requirement is often greater than the operating requirement. The power of the motor for starting can be determined from Fig. 6.10, which has been made from experimental data. It has been found from experiment that this type of horizontal conveyor will transport 1000 ft tons per hr per hp. If the material is to be conveyed up an incline, the power to elevate the material must be added.

Due to slight variations in weight and spring constants, the natural frequency of a conveyor is usually not exactly that of the assumed value. A variable speed pulley is installed on the motor, and an ammeter is used to measure the current. The natural frequency of the conveyor is determined by varying the drive speed until the lowest ammeter reading is obtained.

In the heavier units it is necessary to use hydraulic dampers that have very little movement while the conveyor is operating at normal speed. They become operative when the speed is below this value during starting and stopping periods. The bed tends to come to rest by decreasing its amplitude and maintaining its natural frequency while the driving unit must come to rest at constant amplitude as the frequency decreases. These two conditions are not compatable. The damper permits the driving unit and bed to come to rest, or to start from rest, independently of each other.

An axis of bed motion measured 30 deg from the horizontal produces a favorable combination of vertical and horizontal velocity components of free particles.

Chapter 7 | # THRUSTOR BRAKE

7.1. *Introduction*

Thrustor brakes are used in elevators, cranes, bridges, turn-tables, machine tools, and other rotating machines. In order to make the brake operate automatically in case of a power failure, a spring is used to set the brake, and a Thrustor is used to release it. In this machine it is convenient to use a compression spring, but of greater importance is the fact that a compression spring is more

Fig. 7.1. Thrustor brake.
[Courtesy General Electric Co.]

reliable than a tension spring. If a compression spring breaks, the broken coils will come into contact, and the spring will be partially effective.

The Thrustor is a hydraulic unit, and its smooth operation keeps shock to a minimum. Thrustors can be obtained with a time delay so that, after the motor current is turned off, the moving parts are allowed to slow down before the brake is applied.

Smaller brakes are usually fitted with a solenoid instead of a Thrustor (Fig. 7.2).

Fig. 7.2. Solenoid brake.
[Courtesy General Electric Co.]

7.2. *Specifications*

The torque for continuous operation at 800 rpm is to be 325 lb-ft.

A drum 11 in. in diameter and 5 in. wide is used in the General Electric brake of this capacity.

Shoe clearance at the center of the shoe is to be $\frac{1}{16}$ in. or a little less.

Friction material is to be $\frac{3}{8}$ in. thick, and non-scoring brass rivets should be used.

Arc of contact of each shoe is to be 110 deg.

Factor of safety. A brake is usually expected to be one of the most rugged components of a machine. It must function not only during normal operation but must be relied upon if some other part of the machine fails. In designing a manually operated brake, possible variations in the state of mind of the operator would have to be considered, but in a Thrustor brake a spring is used to supply the braking force. Some shock is present but it is not great because friction lining separates the shoes from the drum, and the Thrustor action is smooth. A factor of safety of 3 is adequate.

7.3. *Force Analysis*

In order to make the force analysis it is necessary to assume the pin locations, and if a poor choice is made it may be necessary to make a second analysis. To prevent the shoes from dragging when the brake is released, the shoe hinge bolts are usually pulled up tight. During braking, the shoe may or may not be pivoted, depending on the degree of tightness of the bolt. The variation in forces resulting from different types of analysis will often be less than those resulting from the variation in coefficients of friction which, according to Table 7.1, are approximately ± 15% for most linings.

Only the pin forces on the self-energizing shoe need be analyzed since the brake must be designed for rotation in either direction. For a symmetrical brake, the forces on the self-energizing arms and shoe are always larger than on the arms and shoe that are not self-energizing. If the brake is to operate during either direction of rotation, either shoe can be self-energizing. Making the arms and pins for the right and left shoes identical also decreases the cost by increasing the number of duplicate parts.

7.4. *Drum*

The drum is to be made of a good grade of cast iron, and designed to promote cooling. When the drum is to be mounted on a tapered shaft, a lock washer should be used under the nut to prevent it from loosening. The slot in the hub, Fig. 7.1, is provided to receive the edge of a washer, and after the nut is tightened, a portion of the washer is bent up against a flat face of the nut. The drum should be put on with a press fit if the shaft is straight. Set screws are seldom used, because the rim is usually as wide as the hub which makes drilling and tapping difficult or impossible.

TABLE 7.1
FRICTION MATERIALS SELECTION CHART

Style Number	100	140	150	200	230	232	240	242	300	304	350	354	400	404	450	454	505	510	600	751	900
Type of brake or clutch — Cast iron or steel drums and discs	disc cone band	disc cone band	disc cone band	disc cone band	disc cone band	cone band	disc cone band	cone band	band	band	disc cone	disc cone	band	band	disc cone	disc cone	band	band	disc cone band	disc	disc cone band
Type of surface — † Furnished standard with ground surface	†	†	†	†	†	†	†	†			†	†			†	†	†	†	† Note 2	†	†
STRUCTURE (R = rigid moulded, SF = semi-flexible, F = flexible)	R	R	R	R	R	SF	R	SF	F	F	SF	SF	SF	SF	SF	SF	F	F	SF	R	SF
Coefficient of friction (‡ Running in oil)	0.25 ±.05	0.40 ±.07	0.45 ±.07	0.40 ±.07	0.45 ±.07	0.45 ±.07	0.40 ±.07	0.40 ±.07	0.40 ±.07	0.20‡ ±.07	0.35 ±.07	0.20‡ ±.07	0.45 ±.07	0.20‡ ±.07	0.45 ±.07	0.20‡ ±.07	0.45 ±.07	0.45 ±.07	0.45 ±.07	0.35 ±.07	0.45 ±.07
Facings — Thickness		Note 3	Note 3	1/8"–3/8"	1/8"–3/8"						3/8"–5/16"	3/8"–5/16"			3/8"–1"	3/4"–1"			1/8"–1"	1/8"–1/2"	1/4"–1/2"
Facings — Max. diam.	35"	35"	35"	40"	16"		20"				to 1/4" thk. 23"; 5/16" thk. 15"	to 1/4" thk. 23"; 5/16" thk. 15"			12"	12"			36"	36"	Note 4
Band or blocks — Thickness		3/8"–4"			1/8"–3/8"	1/8"–3/8"	1/8"–3/8"		1/8"–5/16"	1/8"–5/16"			3/8"–1 1/2"	3/8"–1"			5/32"–1/2"	5/32"–1/2"	1/8"–1"		1/4"–1/2"
Band or blocks — Width		1"–24"			1"–12"	1"–12"			1"–24"	1"–24"			2"–12"	2"–12"			1"–12"	1"–12"	1"–24"		1 1/4"–12"
Band or blocks — Max. length (See Note 5)	120° of circ., but not over 24" long chord. max. area 600 sq. in.			10'–6"	120°: not over 28" long arc	10'–6"	120°: not over 28" long arc	10'–6"	25 & 50 ft. rolls	25 & 50 ft. rolls			To 1/2" thk., 6" wide & less, 25' & 50' rolls; over 1/2" thk., all widths, 25' rolls	To 1/2" thk., 6" wide & less, 25' & 50' rolls; over 1/2" thk., all widths, 25' rolls			25' & 50' rolls to 3/8 x 6, over, 25' rolls	25' & 50' rolls to 3/8 x 6, over, 25' rolls & 50' rolls	25' rolls under 1/2" thk., or 8 1/2" wide, 25' & 50' rolls		6" wide & less, 25' & 50' rolls; over, 25' rolls
Type of service	dry	dry	dry	dry	dry	dry	dry	dry	dry	oil	dry oil	oil	dry	oil	dry oil	oil	dry	dry	dry	dry oil	dry
Max. rubbing speed ft/min	5000	7500	7500	5000	5000	5000	5000	5000	5000	5000	5000	3000	7500	5000	5000	3000	5000	7500	3000	5000	5000
Max. drum temp. °F for constant operation	750	750	750	500	500	500	500	500	250	500	500	500	500	500	500	500	500	500	350	500	500
Max. pressure: psi	150	150	150	100	100	100	100	100	50	100	100	50	100	100	100	100	75	100	100	100	100
Resistance to shock (M = Med., E = Excel., G = Good)	E	E	E	G	G	G	G	G	M	M	G	M	G	M	M	M	G	G	E	G	G
Rate of wear (M = Med., G = Good, E = Excel., V = Var., depend. on amt. of oil)	E	E	E	M	E	M	E	M	M	V	G	V	G	V	G	V	G	G	E	G	E

See Note 1 (Type of surface, Styles 100–150)

For short periods of operation will withstand an additional 250°F

Note 1 — Blocks over 12" wide cannot be ground on I.D.; Blocks 24" wide, less than 1/2" thick, cannot be ground, I.D. or O.D.

Note 2 — Style 600 Lining is furnished unground over 18" wide.

Note 3 — Full moulded to 1/2" thick and 35" O.D. Saw cut from slab over 1/2" thick to 2 1/2" and max. O.D. of 24".

Note 4 — 1/4" thick–24 diam. Max. over 1/4" thick to 3/8" thick–12" diam. Max.

Note 5 — Standard length rolls are ±5 Ft. of nominal length.

\# — Style No. 900 lining less than 2" wide cannot be furnished greater than 1/4" thick.

Table 7.1 reproduced courtesy of Johns-Manville Corp.

7.5. *Arms, Pins, and Shoes*

The arms, shoe hinge bolts, and shoes are dimensionally inter-related. One method of procedure is to determine the diameter of the shoe hinge bolt by assuming the arm thickness and the thickness of that part of the shoe that engages the bolt. The width of the arm can then be determined, and if the arm does not cover the edge of the drum to prevent it from coming off the shaft in case of looseness, the bottom curve of the arm should be shaped to cover it.

The shoe is to be made of cast iron. A shoe that has adequate stiffness and sound casting qualities can be sketched and then checked for stress. The ribs add to the stiffness, strength, and cooling capacity of the shoe. Recommendations for size and spacing of rivets can be found in the *Society of Automotive Engineers Handbook*. Non-scoring brass rivets, ³⁄₁₆ in. size, spaced as shown in Fig. 7.3, would be satisfactory.

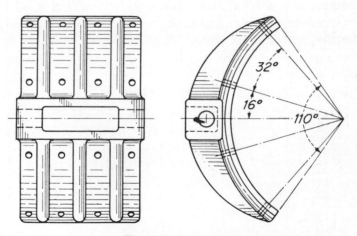

Fig. 7.3. Brake shoe.

7.6. *Spring*

The spring force determined in the force analysis is for setting the brake. In order to release the brake, the spring must be compressed further. Since the increase in force increases the required capacity of the Thrustor, the increase should be kept to a minimum, but a small spring rate requires a long spring. Another reason for keeping the spring rate low is that the braking capacity decreases as the linings wear. Wear of the linings can be taken up by adjusting the spring-seat nut on the center rod, but by good design, this adjust-

ment will be required at infrequent intervals. A reasonable com-
promise is to assume that the spring force increases 15% from
brake-set to brake-released position.

The pitch of the coils should be chosen to allow some additional
deflection beyond the brake-released position but the spring should
close up solidly before the yield point is reached. The stall thrust of
the thrustor is considerably greater than the rated thrust, and if the
spring is not designed as indicated above, improper setting could
result in a damaged spring.

7.7. *Selection of Thrustor*

The correct Thrustor can probably be selected at the first trial
if energy considerations are applied. The spring force and travel
are known, as are the Thrustor force and travel, Table 7.2. Not all
of the Thrustor stroke can be used, because it is necessary to reserve
the bottom part of the stroke to allow for wear. It can be seen that
when the linings are worn, the arms come closer together when the
brake is set, and the bell crank moves lower. If the piston reaches
the bottom of its stroke, the brake will not set. As wear takes place,
the spring-seat nut can be adjusted, but it should not be so critical
that frequent adjustment is required to keep the brake operating.
If about ¾ in. of the stroke is reserved for this, frequent adjustment
will not be necessary. (For Thrustor details see Fig. 7.4.)

7.8. *Bell Crank*

The bell crank and other parts of the brake that are subjected to the
thrust force should be designed to withstand the stall thrust. The
force to release the brake should be based on approximately 90% of
the rated thrust. The reason for this will be explained later. This
force and the brake-released spring force can be used to determine
the ratio of the arms of the bell crank. The length of the long arm is
determined by space requirements; the Thrustor must clear the
brake arms.

It is desirable that the rocking motion of the Thrustor be kept at
a minimum. This can be accomplished by making the bell crank in
the form of an isosceles triangle, Fig. 7.5(b). Since the Thrustor is
at one side of the brake, the forces within the brake are unbalanced
and the arms tend to move away from the Thrustor. A stop must be

Top lug can be pinned to either a movable or a fixed clevis.

Leather seals check entrance of dirt, water, etc., into the tank.

Bronze guide-bushings

Conical baffle minimizes turbulence in the oil.

Oil-level plug

Oil tube directs oil flow from chamber above piston to impeller chamber.

Spacers limit the travel of the piston. Additional spacers may be used to shorten the stroke.

Tank (cast-iron for units rated 100–800 lb) forms a cylinder in which the piston slides.

Impeller drive-shaft

Shoulder forms stop for piston on downstroke.

Valve which is actuated by coil-spring return to normal position, to by-pass oil above impeller and piston, thus determining the time of return on downstroke.

Straight-blade impeller together with impeller-housing operates in either direction as a centrifugal pump which exerts pressure under the piston and causes it to rise. Motor cannot be overloaded—if Thrustor stalls in any position, the impeller spins freely in oil.

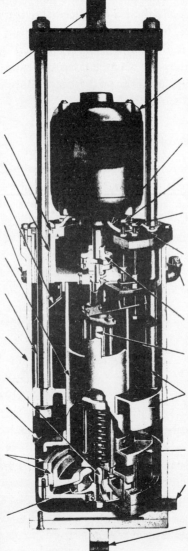

Totally enclosed, ball-bearing motor for driving impeller.

Adapter plate for mounting motor.

Adjustment for time-delay that controls speed of downstroke.

Adjustment for time-delay that controls speed of up-stroke.

Spacers under retaining plate allow for tightening seals around push-rods.

Filler plug

Disk-coupling connecting motor-shaft to impeller-shaft.

Cover-pipe over drive shaft

Movable members (cast-iron piston, steel push-rods and cross-bar). Oil pressure from pump below causes the piston to rise, forcing the push-rods and cross-bar with it and giving the desired motion.

Cast-iron impeller-housing directs flow of oil from impeller to chamber under piston.

Drain plug

Base for clevis mounting. Interchangeable base for rigid mounting can be supplied. Thrustors rated 100 lb and higher can be tilted 45 deg either side of vertical.

Fig. 7.4. Thrustor details. [Courtesy General Electric Co.]

TABLE 7.2

Thrustor	Rated Thrust, lb	Stall Thrust, lb	A	B	C	D	E	F	G	H	J	M	N	P	R	S	X
1	100	135	18 15/16	7 7/8	13 13/16	12 1/2	2	7	1	2 3/4	1/2	1 1/2	1/2	1	1 1/2	7 3/4	4 5/8
2	200	260	25 15/16	9 1/2	18 7/8	17 5/16	3	8 1/2	1 1/4	3 1/4	5/8	1 1/2	1/2	1	1 1/2	9 1/4	5 1/2
3	400	560	27 7/16	10 3/4	20 1/4	18 11/16	3	9 3/4	1 1/4	3 3/4	3/4	1 1/2	1/2	1	1 1/2	10 1/2	6 5/16
4	600	780	28 15/16	12	21	19 7/16	3	10 1/2	1 1/4	4 1/16	7/8	1 1/2	1/2	1	1 1/2	11 1/4	6 5/16

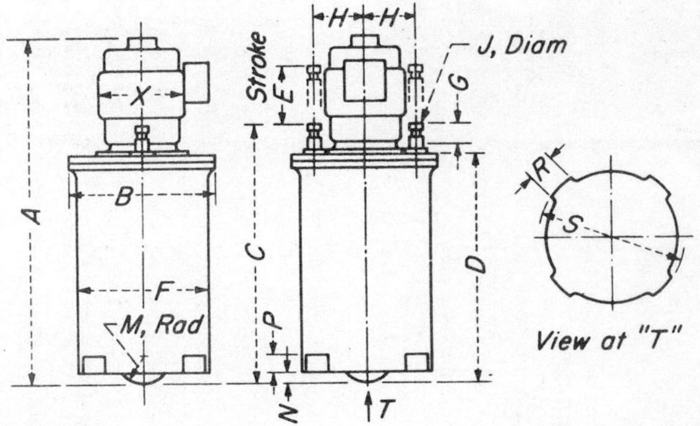

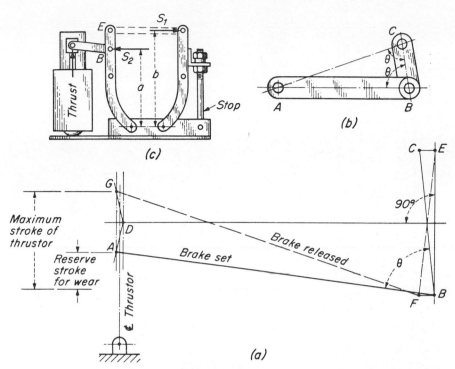

Fig. 7.5. Bell crank.

provided to hold the arms that are on the side opposite the Thrustor. The brake, Fig. 7.5(a), is released as follows. When A moves to D, with the left arm in set position, the bell crank pivots about B, and C moves to E, thus releasing the right shoe. At this position the stop is reached, making E a fixed point. Movement from D to G swings B to F while the crank pivots about E, thus releasing the left shoe.

This analysis is not quite correct, since B is closer than E to the pivot point of the arm, Fig. 7.5(c). The left shoe will be pulled slightly farther away from the drum than the right shoe, and the clearances can be made equal by making GD shorter. However, this shortening of GD is not necessary since the final adjustment is made at the stop when the brake is assembled, and the clearances can be made equal. For the same reason the force to release the left shoe is greater than the spring force S_1; the force to release the left shoe is $S_2 = S_1b/a$. For average proportions this force can be accounted for by using 90% of the rated thrust in the determination of the ratio of the bell crank arms.

Chapter 8

GEAR REDUCERS

8.1. *Introduction*

A gear reducer is either of the general-purpose type or is designed for a specific use as an integral part of a machine. An automobile differential is an example of the latter type. In the design of integral reducers, it is often more economical to buy standard gears and incorporate them in the machine than to design and build them. Many sizes and types of gears can be obtained from numerous manufacturers; the integral pinion and shaft, Fig. 8.1, is an example. The shaft is made to fit standard bearings. In this chapter, only the general purpose type is considered, however most of the discussion applies to reducers designed for specific purposes.

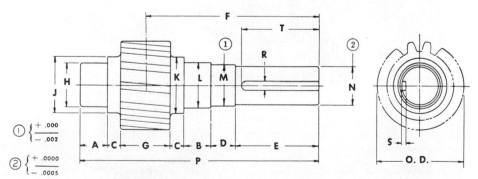

Fig. 8.1. Integral pinion and shaft.
[Courtesy Foote Bros. Gear and Machine Corp.]

Fig. 8.2 illustrates an application of one of the basic principles of design, i.e., to design from the inside out. Even though the components are interrelated and certain considerations must be kept in mind throughout the design, the components are designed in the following order: gears, shafts, selection of rolling-contact bearings or design of sleeve bearings, and housing, i.e., (innermost) gears first and (outer) housing last.

8.2. *Shafting*

Gears usually fail because of wear rather than because of the tooth breakage. Even the highest grade gears will not last long if they are not properly lubricated or not held in proper mesh. Hence rigidity of shafts and housing and accurate machining are essential. Since the rigidity of a shaft is proportional to the fourth power of the diameter, the low speed shaft is seldom the critical member.

Fig. 8.2. Double worm gear reducer.
[Courtesy Link-Belt Co.]

The following equation is sometimes used to determine the maximum allowable deflection of a shaft:

$$\text{maximum allowable deflection} = \frac{\text{bearing span}}{2500}$$

In Fig. 8.3, the pinion shaft deflection is kept to a minimum by splitting the herringbone pinion and putting the halves near the bearings. In Fig. 8.4, the left half of the herringbone pinion is extended to the bearing to add to the stiffness of the shaft. Three bearings are used on the pinion shaft in Fig. 8.5.

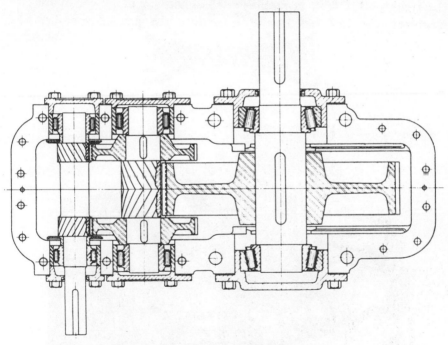

Fig. 8.3. Two-stage herringbone gear reducer.
[Courtesy Hewitt-Robins, Inc.]

The bending moment in a shaft, due to the overhanging load, varies considerably in different applications. One assumption that is usually adequate is to design for a bending moment that is equal to one and one half times the torque.

It is desirable that the gear be pressed on the shaft to produce more accurate tooth engagement, but it is not always safe to assume that a press fit will prevent a gear from moving axially on the shaft. In Fig. 8.14, the hub of the herringbone gear presses against the

Fig. 8.4. Three-stage herringbone gear reducer.
[Courtesy of Palmer-Bee Co.]

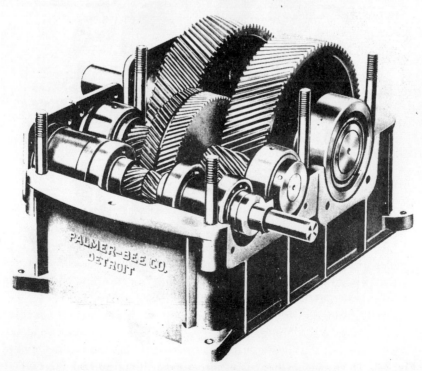

Fig. 8.5. Two-stage herringbone gear reducer.
[Courtesy of Palmer-Bee Co.]

Fig. 8.6. Two-stage gear reducer. [Courtesy Foote Bros. Gear and Machine Corp.]

Fig. 8.7. Three-stage gear reducer. [Courtesy Foote Bros. Gear and Machine Corp.]

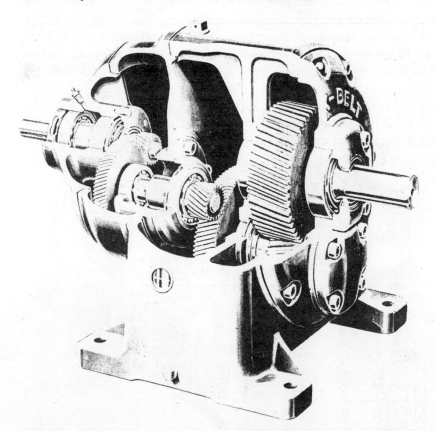

Fig. 8.8. Three-stage, in-line, helical gear reducer. [Courtesy Link-Belt Co.]

inner race of the bearing on one side, and against a space collar on the other side. On the intermediate shaft, the bevel gear hub presses against the inner race of the bearing.

Housings are designed to provide adequate stiffness, and often external or internal ribs are used, Figs. 8.6, 8.7, and 8.8.

8.3. *Bearings*

Thrust must always be considered in the design of a gear reducer. Thrust is inherent in worm and helical gears, and provision must be made for the bearings to take thrust in either direction. In Fig. 8.9, the mounting is designed so that the left bearing will take thrust in either direction while the right bearing is relieved of thrust. Two other methods for mounting a bearing to take thrust in either direction are shown in Figs. 8.10 and 8.11. If one bearing is to take thrust in one direction and the other bearing is to take thrust in the other direction, some end play must be allowed to provide for inaccuracies and unequal expansion of the parts due to heating. Shims sometimes are used in assembly to control such inaccuracies.

In herringbone gears the thrust is balanced within the gears, but there may be external thrust on the output or input shaft and

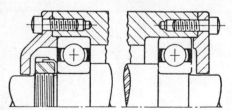

Fig. 8.9. Ball bearing mounting. The left bearing will take thrust in either direction. [Courtesy New Departure]

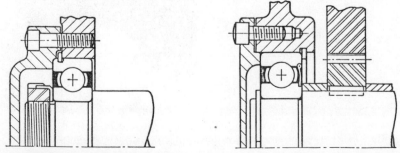

Figs. 8.10, 8.11. Ball bearing mounted to take thrust in either direction. [Courtesy New Departure]

provision must be made to carry this thrust. The mountings of only one shaft, usually the output shaft, are designed to carry thrust. The other shafts must be allowed to float so that the right and left halves of the gears carry equal loads. In Fig. 8.3, the tapered roller bearings on the output shaft will carry thrust in either direction. The input and intermediate shafts are mounted on roller bearings which allow axial adjustment of the gears. In Fig. 8.12, the sleeve bearings on the output shaft are designed to carry thrust at their inner ends. The input and intermediate shafts are mounted on roller bearings.

8.4. *Lubrication*

Adequate lubrication can usually be provided in the average helical or herringbone reducer with antifriction bearings by allowing the gear to dip into the oil in the housing. In two- and three-

Fig. 8.12. Two-stage herringbone gear reducer.
[Courtesy Lufkin Foundry and Machine Co.]

stage reducers, the output gear often turns too slowly to throw the oil and it is necessary to let one of the intermediate gears dip into the oil.

A more adequate system is required when journal bearings are used. In Fig. 8.12, oil scrapers are used to take oil from the sides of the gear and direct it into grooves in the cover; these grooves lead to all of the bearings. In Fig. 8.13, the two large gears have scrapers which direct the oil into grooves in the inner surface of the housing. Oil thrown on the cover runs into the groove at the left end of the housing. The oil passes through the bearings before returning to the sump.

Fig. 8.13. Three-stage herringbone gear reducer.
[Courtesy Link-Belt Co.]

The bevel pinion shaft, Fig. 8.14, is mounted on two tapered roller bearings, the arrangement being that shown in Fig. 8.15. Due to centrifugal force, a tapered roller bearing will pump oil toward the base of the rotating cone, the amount of pumping action depending on the cone diameter, cone angle, and speed of rotation. At slow speeds, oil thrown from the housing into the first bearing will pass through and lubricate the second bearing, but at high speeds the left bearing will not be adequately lubricated. In Fig.

8.14, a shelf is provided in the cover which catches oil thrown by
the gears and allows the oil to drip through holes into the grooves
at the end of the housing. These grooves lead the oil into the space
between the bearings. In some cases the oil pressure built up by a
tapered roller bearing is great enough to cause leakage through the
seal. When there is a possibility of leakage, a drain connecting
with the sump should be provided.

Fig. 8.14. Two-stage bevel and herringbone gear reducer.
[Courtesy Palmer-Bee Co.]

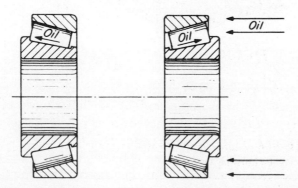

Fig. 8.15. Tapered roller bearings, showing direction of oil pumping.

8.5. *Cooling*

All energy losses in a gear reducer are converted into heat which must be dissipated. The thermal horsepower capacity of a single stage helical or herringbone reducer is given by the equation[1]

$$\text{hp} = 3.265 C \sqrt[1.5]{F} - 0.0483 C^{1.5} F$$

where C = center distance, in.
  F = face width, in. Where the clearance between the housing and gear face is more than normal, the thermal rating may be based on the maximum face width of gear that the housing will accommodate.

This equation applies to separate enclosed, splash-lubricated, reducers or increasers where the pitch line velocity is less than 4000

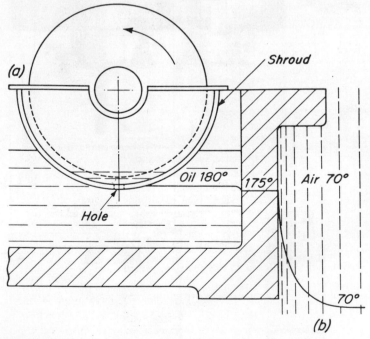

Fig. 8.16. Temperature gradient in a housing. The shroud is used to reduce the churning loss.

<hr />

[1] "Standard Practice Helical and Herringbone Gear Speed Reducers," American Gear Manufacturers Association, 420.02, February, 1951. The standards of the AGMA are revised from time to time.

fpm and the pinion speed is less than 3600 rpm. Since this is an empirical equation based on average conditions, i.e., external area of housing and room temperature, the designer should not be misled by the number of significant figures in the constants.

At high speeds, the churning loss is excessive and steps should be taken to reduce such loss. A disc oil slinger that dips into the oil will throw oil with less churning loss than that produced by a gear. Churning loss can be reduced by means of a sheet metal shroud, Fig. 8.16(a). The oil level inside of the shroud depends on the speed of the gear and the size of the entrance hole.

Fig. 8.17. Worm reducer with fan and cooling fins. In many worm reducers, the worm is immersed in oil, and special seals or packings are used to prevent leakage along the worm shaft. In this example, both ends of the worm shaft extend through the housing, and, because of the fan and cover, one end is not easily accessible for packing adjustment. For this reason, the oil level is below the worm, and oil slingers are fitted on the worm shaft. This makes special seals unnecessary and also reduces the churning loss. [Courtesy Palmer-Bee Co.]

The maximum operating temperature of the oil is 180°F and the room temperature is usually 70°F, Fig. 8.16(b)[1]. When the heat is not dissipated naturally, artificial means for dissipation must be provided. The worm reducer, Fig. 8.17, contains a fan on the high speed shaft which blows air across the cooling fins on the oil sump.

In some worm reducers, air is blown through tubes that pass through the oil in the housing. If the unit is operating in an atmosphere containing dust and other foreign matter, a coating which acts as an insulator often forms on the inside of the tubes. If

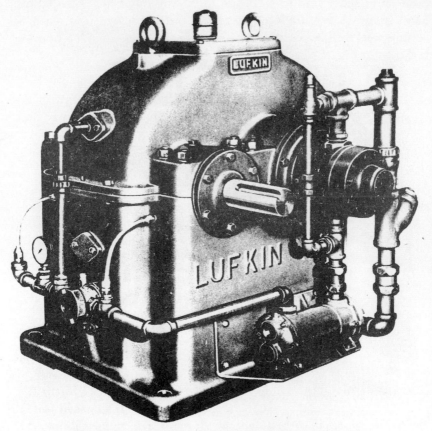

Fig. 8.18. High-speed reducer with oil pump and cooler.
[Courtesy Lufkin Foundry and Machine Co.]

---

[1] The temperature gradiant curve follows that of "Cleveland Worm Gear Speed Reducers," Catalog 400.

an insulating layer forms on external fins, it is at once apparent and can be removed with a brush.

In order to prevent churning losses and to produce a convenient means for cooling the oil, high speed reducers and increasers are often made with an external lubricating system. The high speed reducer, Fig. 8.18, has an oil pump on the low speed shaft, and an oil cooler on the bracket near the bottom of the housing.

8.6. *Housing*

The primary functions of a housing are to hold the shafts in a fixed position in space and to facilitate lubrication and heat dissipation. Most housings are made of cast iron, but for severe uses, such as certain steel mill applications, welded steel is used. Such a housing is shown in Fig. 8.19.

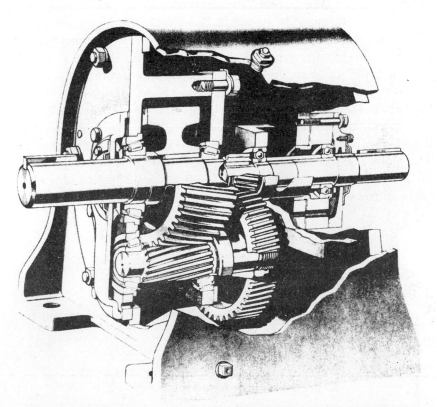

Fig. 8.19. Two-stage, in-line, helical gear reducer with welded steel housing. [Courtesy Falk Corp.]

Some of the factors that must be considered in the design of a housing are strength, rigidity, casting qualities, cooling capacity, ease of casting, ease of machining, assembly and disassembly, lubrication, and multiple use.

The housing should be deep enough to allow sedimentation, and it is desirable that the bottom should slope toward the drain plug. An oil level plug should be installed at the proper level, and a convenient means for adding oil should be provided. Sight level indicators are sometimes used. Unless special seals are used, the oil level should always be kept below the level of the lowest seal. A breather should be installed in the cover to prevent the air pressure from building up due to heating. An increase in air pressure may cause the oil to leak through the seals. If convenient, an inspection cover for casual inspection of the gears should be provided.

When a housing is designed for good casting qualities, it usually has sufficient strength and rigidity. However, if there is any doubt as to its strength and rigidity, these should be checked.

The order in which the machining is done is shown in Fig. 8.20. The bottom surface of the housing is machined first, and then the top surface is machined. After the bottom of the cover is machined, the cover and housing are bolted together. These are usually doweled at the ends, and thus the parts are not interchangeable. The plane surfaces on the sides are then finished. It is desirable that all of the surfaces on a side lie in a single plane. The holes are then bored through the housing. These holes can be bored accurately

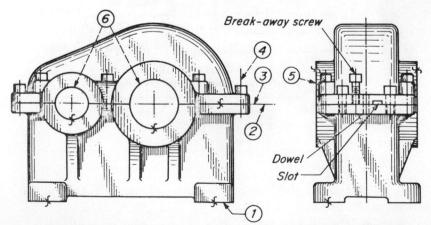

Fig. 8.20. Housing with numbers showing order of machining operations.

enough to serve as bearing mountings. Non-hardening liquid gaskets are usually used between the housing and cover. The thickness of this type of gasket is so slight that the bearing mounting is not affected.

To facilitate removal of the cover, some manufacturers provide a break-away screw, Fig. 8.20. Some manufacturers machine a slot in the cover so that it can be loosened by tapping with a cold chisel, while others recommend that the lifting eye bolts be used to pull the cover.

When a series of reducers is designed, the number of housings is kept to a minimum. Each housing is designed to accommodate a series of gear ratios. The two housings shown in Figs. 8.6 and 8.7 are made from the same casting, while the castings for those in Figs. 8.4 and 8.5 are made from a combination pattern. Whenever possible, the housing should be designed so that the gears, shafts, and bearings can be assembled before placing them in the housing.

The nine standard assemblies for the single stage helical or herringbone reducer are shown in Fig. 8.21. For a single housing to accommodate the assemblies, it is necessary that it be symmetrical about its longitudinal center plane.

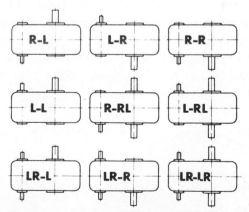

Fig. 8.21. Standard assembly diagrams for single stage, parallel shaft reducers. [Courtesy Hewitt-Robins, Inc.]

8.7. *Problem*

The statement of the gear reducer problem will be furnished by the instructor.

Chapter 9

30-TON YOKE
RIVETER

9.1. *Toggle Linkage*

A common type of pneumatic yoke riveter is shown in Figs. 9.1 and 9.2. Since the formation of the head of a rivet requires a large force over an appreciable part of the die stroke, a simple toggle linkage is not satisfactory for large riveters. The toggle linkage shown in Fig. 9.2 produces the die displacement pattern shown at the lower left of the figure. The squeeze-die stroke curve, Fig. 9.3, was obtained experimentally from a 30-ton riveter having the type of toggle linkage shown in Fig. 9.2. A minimum of 30 tons of force is provided over the final half inch of die travel which is sufficient for forming the head of a ¾-in. structural rivet.

9.2. *Required Force*

The force required to drive hot button-head rivets is shown in Table 9.1.

TABLE 9.1
FORCE REQUIRED TO DRIVE HOT BUTTON-HEAD RIVETS

Riveter Tonnage	Rivet Size, in., Safe Practice for Average Conditions	
	Structural	Steam Tight
30	⅝ to ¾	½
50	⅞ to 1	⅝
80	1⅛ to 1¼	1
100	1½	1⅛

The heads, *A*, *B*, and *C*, Fig. 9.4, represent what is considered good practice for cold riveting. Button-driven heads should be avoided because they require considerable force which will often damage the work and generally lower the quality and strength of the rivet. Rivets used for cold riveting should be cold-formed and must be annealed after forming and before driving.

Fig. 9.1. 30-ton yoke riveter.
[Courtesy Hanna Engineering Works]

The force required to cold form the heads *A*, *B*, and *C* will, of course, depend upon the material in the rivet. For commonly used annealed steel rivets, the forces listed in Table 9.2 are safe. Over-driving of rivets should always be avoided. The driven heads *A*, *B*, and *C* are as strong as the rivet shank in a straight tensile pull.

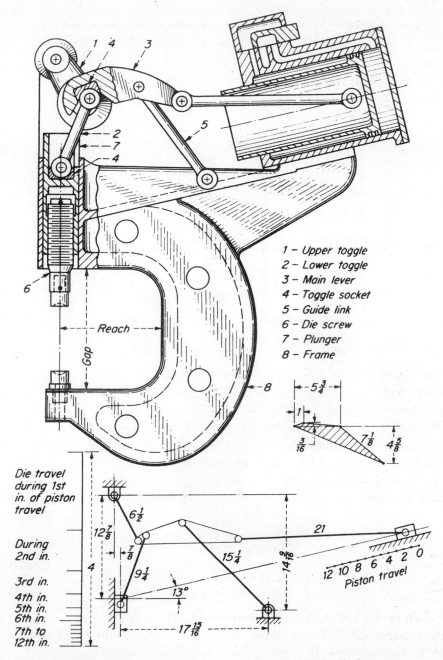

1 – Upper toggle
2 – Lower toggle
3 – Main lever
4 – Toggle socket
5 – Guide link
6 – Die screw
7 – Plunger
8 – Frame

Fig. 9.2. Yoke riveter, showing toggle linkage and die displacement diagram.

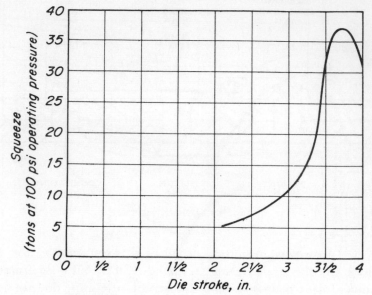

Fig. 9.3. Tonnage-stroke chart, 30-ton riveter.

9.3. *Design Details*

The turning pairs formed by the main lever with the upper and lower toggles, Fig. 9.2, are so close to each other that conventional pin connections are not feasible. The upper end of the lower toggle fits into a lumen bronze socket. For smooth action and compactness, it is desirable that the lower end of the lower toggle fit inside the frame. A lumen bronze socket also is used here. Since the sockets will not carry a tensile load, it is necessary to provide pins to carry the tensile load during retraction of the plunger.

TABLE 9.2
FORCE REQUIRED TO DRIVE COLD RIVETS

Rivet size, inches	³⁄₁₆	¼	⁵⁄₁₆	⅜	⁷⁄₁₆	½	⅝	¾	⅞	1	1¼
Force, tons	4.5	7	12	16	22	29	44	64	87	112	165

To prevent thread damage, the engagement of the die screw in the plunger should be 1½ times the diameter of the screw. Damage to the threads through carelessness of the operator can be prevented by providing a pin near the top of the screw which will make contact with a shoulder in the counterbored plunger when the screw is

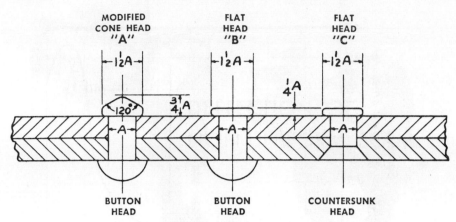

Fig. 9.4. Cold-driven rivets.
[Courtesy Hanna Engineering Works]

lowered to a predetermined position. After assembly, the pin is driven into the screw through a hole drilled through the frame and plunger. If it is necessary to disassemble the unit, the pin can be driven out in the same manner.

9.4. *Design for Economy*

Riveters are included in the class of machines that are designed for good quality and limited production. A company which builds riveters would plan to cover a broad range of requirements. Table 9.3 represents a group of Hanna riveters. Three operating units that are similar but of different capacity are incorporated in forty-eight different frames. This reduces engineering and production costs and also facilitates service in the field. These same operating units are also used in more specialized types of riveters as shown in Figs. 9.5 and 9.6.

TABLE 9.3
RIVETER SIZES

Reach, inches	Gap, inches		
	30 ton	50 ton	80 ton
12	12, 15, 18	12, 15, 18	15, 18, ..
18	12, 15, 18	15, 18, ..	15, 18, ..
24	15, 18, 24	15, 18, 21	18, 21, 24
30	18, 21, 24	18, 21, 24	18, 21, ..
36	18, 21, 24	18, 21, 24	18, 21, 24
48	.. .. ..	18, 21, 24	18, 21, 24
60	.. .. ..	.. .. ..	24 .. ..

Fig. 9.5. This riveter is adapted for work where space on both sides of the rivet is restricted, e.g., in riveting channels or beams flange to flange. [Courtesy Hanna Engineering Works]

Fig. 9.6. This riveter is used when the rivets are within 4 in. of the edge and the space below and behind them is restricted, e.g., a door ring of a boiler. [Courtesy Hanna Engineering Works]

9.5. *Problem*

This problem consists of the design of a 30-ton riveter with 12 in. reach, 15 in. gap, and operating air pressure of 100 psi. The linkage dimensions can be taken from Fig. 9.2.

Chapter 10

DEFLECTION OF
NON-UNIFORM BEAM

10.1. *Introduction*

In engineering practice, analytical solutions sometimes become so involved and time-consuming that graphical or tabular methods are preferred. The determination of the deflection curve of a non-uniform beam often falls into this class and is usually solved graphically. In many other cases where an analytical solution is made, it is desirable to carry through a graphical solution to check for errors. The theory pertaining to graphical integration will be discussed first, and then an example will be worked to illustrate the procedure.

10.2. *Graphical Integration*

The curve shown in Fig. 10.1(a) is to be integrated. The curve is divided into segments by erecting arbitrarily chosen perpendiculars BB_1, CC_1, etc. The points P and R are arbitrarily chosen in line with OX, and points 1, 2, 3, etc. are obtained by projecting horizontally from the mid-points (the mean of the abscissas) of the lines A_1B_1, B_1C_1, etc. The rays $P1$, $P2$, $P3$, etc. represent the chords of the integral curve.

The integral curve, Fig. 10.1(c), is constructed on a base line O_1X_1 by making $O_1b = OB$, $bc = BC$, etc., and then drawing O_1b_1 parallel to $P1$, b_1c_1 parallel to $P2$, etc. It can be seen that this construction is correct if it is remembered that the integral curve represents the growth in area under the original curve. The height bb_1 is equal to the product of the length O_1b and the slope of O_1b_1, but $O_1b = OB$, and the slope of O_1b_1 is proportional to the height y. The distances bb_1, cc_1, etc., represent the area under the curve shown in Fig. 10.1(a) to some scale.

The scales s and m for the original curve are assumed. If OB is made one unit long, the unit area shown at Fig. 10.1(a) will represent ms actual units.

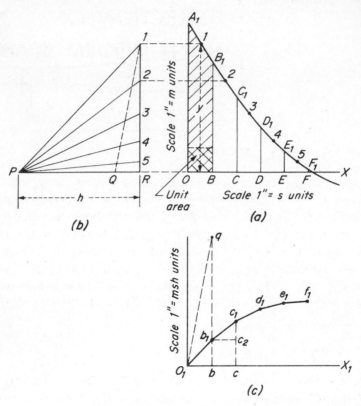

Fig. 10.1. Graphical integration.

If QR is made equal to OB and O_1q is drawn parallel to $Q1$, bq will equal y and will represent the area OBB_1A_1 to the scale 1 in. = ms. Now, if h is made larger than QR, say four times as large, bb_1 will be only one fourth as large as bq and it will be necessary to multiply the scale by h, giving 1 in. = msh. Similarly, the height c_2c_1 represents the area BCC_1B_1, and the height cc_1 represents the total area OCC_1A_1.

The determination of the deflection curve for the non-uniform shaft, Fig. 10.2(a), is a typical example of graphical integration. All of the scales refer to the original drawing which was made approximately twice the size of the drawing reproduced here. Values of M/EI were calculated for different stations along the shaft and plotted at Fig. 10.2(c). In order to better suit the changes in curvature, reference stations at changes of section and at concen-

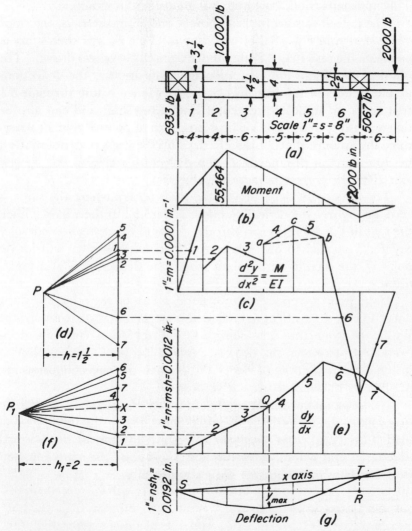

Fig. 10.2. Determination of deflection curve of non-uniform beam, using graphical integration.

trated loads were chosen. For greater accuracy in the deflection curve, a long uniform section should be divided into several sections even though it carries no load. In this example the tapered section was divided in the middle to give the lines *ac* and *cb*. If the tapered section had not been divided, the dotted line *ab* would have resulted and would have introduced an appreciable error. Actually the lines *ac* and *cb* are not straight, because *I* does not vary linearly. This approximation, however, was made in this example.

The pole *P* was arbitrarily chosen, and from the rays, the slope curve shown in Fig. 10.2(e) was drawn. Pole P_1 was then chosen, and from the rays $P_1 1$, $P_1 2$, etc., the deflection curve was drawn. The physical conditions imposed upon the shaft are that the deflections at the centers of the bearings be zero. Hence a line through *ST* represents the undeformed center line of the shaft and can also be taken as the *x* axis. The vertical positions of poles *P* and P_1 determine the amount that *ST* is skewed. This skewness does not matter, because vertical distance from the deflection curve to the skewed axis gives the correct numerical value.

The maximum deflection of the shaft occurs where the slope is zero, i.e., where the deflection curve is parallel to the *x* axis. Since the rays in Fig. 10.2(f) represent the slopes of the deflection curve, a ray $P_1 X$, parallel to *ST*, when projected horizontally, will locate point *Q*, the section on the shaft where the deflection is at a maximum.

If the point *Q* represents zero slope, it can be seen that the slope curve in Fig. 10.2(e) cannot be used in its present state to determine slopes, because the first constant of integration has not been evaluated. In effect, the two constants of integration are evaluated in the deflection curve of Fig. 10.2(g) when the end conditions are applied by drawing the line *ST*.

In the above example the loads lie in one plane, although in many cases the loads lie in several planes. When the latter type of load is analyzed, it is necessary to resolve the forces into vertical and horizontal planes, carry through a solution for each plane, and then combine the deflection curves vectorially.

10.3. *Tabular Method*

Graphical integration is sufficiently accurate for most purposes, but if greater accuracy is desired, a tabular solution can easily be made, using as many stations as desired, to give any desired degree of accuracy. By examining Fig. 10.2, the reader should be able to devise a tabular method. If the space scale and the distances h and h_1 are taken as unity and the actual values of M/EI are used, the resulting values for y will be in actual inches. The values for y must be corrected for the end conditions by calling the value at the right reaction zero, and then subtracting the proportional amount of TR, Fig. 10.2(g), from the values obtained at the other stations. This problem is for the reader to solve.

10.4. *Problem*

A modified steam turbine shaft is shown in Fig. 10.3. An actual turbine shaft of this size has many steps and requires approximately thirty-five stations and the use of a large scale in the solution. The solution for the simplified shaft shown here can be made to a small scale in a reasonable length of time without omitting any of the theory. Shafts as small as this one are usually made from a single forging with a hole bored through the center.

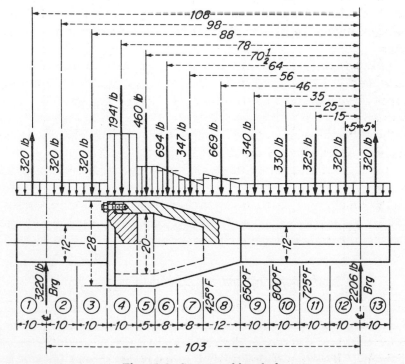

Fig. 10.3. Steam turbine shaft.

The natural frequency of lateral vibration can be obtained by the Rayleigh method[1] if the static deflection curve of the shaft is known, and if it is assumed that this curve is the same as the curve of the vibrating beam. When the beam has ends which hang over, the static deflection curve, Fig. 10.4(a), should not be used. When the beam vibrates, it takes the shape shown at Fig. 10.4(b). A close

(a)   -   *(b)*

Fig. 10.4. Deflection of (a) static shaft and (b) vibrating shaft.

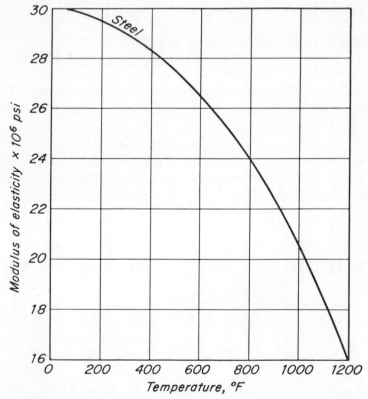

Fig. 10.5. Modulus of elasticity-temperature curve for steel.

---

[1] See W. T. Thomson, *Mechanical Vibrations*, 2nd ed. (Englewood Cliffs, N. J.: Prentice-Hall, Inc., 1953).

approximation to the vibrating deflection curve can be obtained by assuming that the weight of the overhanging ends acts upward as shown in Fig. 10.3.

The weights shown in Fig. 10.3 include attached members, and for simplicity have been taken at the mid-points of the sections. These equivalent concentrated loads can be used to determine the bending moments at the different stations. The values for the modulus of elasticity for the temperatures shown on the shaft can be taken from Fig. 10.5. The normal value of E is to be used at the stations where the temperature is not indicated.

In most cases the deflection due to transverse shear is negligible, but in this case the L/D ratio is small enough to make the deflection appreciable. When shear is included, the equation for the shaft is

$$\frac{d^2y}{dx^2} = \frac{1}{EI}\left(M + K\,\frac{EIW}{AGL}\right)$$

taking $E/G = 2.6$, gives

$$\frac{d^2y}{dx^2} = \frac{M}{EI} + \frac{2.6KW}{AEL}$$

where A is the cross section area, W the weight over a length L, and K the maximum shear stress divided by the average shear stress.

The shear stress is

$$s_s = \frac{VQ}{Ib} = \left(\frac{V}{A}\right)\left(\frac{AQ}{Ib}\right)$$

where V = total vertical shear

I = moment of inertia of entire cross section

b = width at element where stress is desired. In this case the maximum stress is wanted, and $b = 2(R - r)$.

Q = moment, with respect to the neutral axis, of the area of the cross section on the side of the section on which the shearing stress is desired.

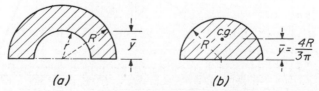

(a)   (b)

Fig. 10.6. Center of gravity of sections.

For a hollow circular shaft, Fig. 10.6(a), the value for Q is

$$Q = \frac{A}{2}\bar{y} = \frac{\pi R^2}{2}\left(\frac{4R}{3\pi}\right) - \frac{\pi r^2}{2}\left(\frac{4r}{3\pi}\right) = \frac{2}{3}(R^3 - r^3)$$

The maximum shear stress is then

$$(s_s)_{max} = \left(\frac{V}{A}\right)\frac{\pi(R^2 - r^2)\,\frac{2}{3}\,(R^3 - r^3)}{\frac{\pi}{4}(R^4 - r^4)2(R - r)} = \left(\frac{V}{A}\right)\frac{4}{3}\frac{R^3 + r^3}{(R^2 + r^2)(R - r)}$$

Dividing this by the average stress V/A and dividing the numerator and denominator by $(R - r)$ gives

$$K = \frac{4}{3}\left(\frac{R^2 + Rr + r^2}{R^2 + r^2}\right) = \frac{4}{3}\left[\frac{1 + r/R + (r/R)^2}{1 + (r/R)^2}\right]$$

Values for K are plotted in Fig. 10.7.

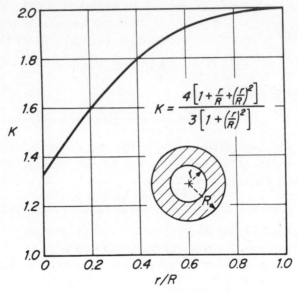

Fig. 10.7. K factor for hollow cylinder.

The natural frequency in rpm is

$$\omega = 187.5\sqrt{\frac{\Sigma\,(Wy)}{\Sigma\,(Wy^2)}}$$

where W is the weight (lb) of an element and y (in.) is the deflection of the center of gravity.

The graphical work can be performed on a sheet of paper 11 by 16 in. as shown in Fig. 10.8. After the work is finished, the sheet can be folded and bound with the computations.

It was stated earlier that the shaft, Fig. 10.3, has been simplified. The analysis of an actual turbine shaft, Fig. 10.10, requires considerable judgment. Some of the factors that must be considered

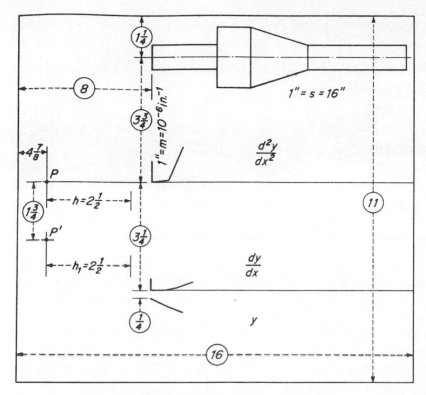

Fig. 10.8. Layout for steam turbine shaft problems.

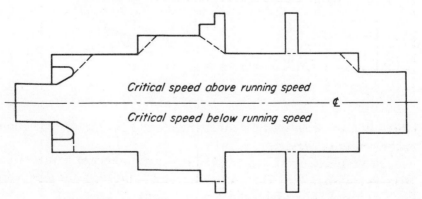

Fig. 10.9. Assumptions that affect the stiffness of a beam.

Fig. 10.10. Spindle for 125,000-kw cross-compound turbine. The overall length is approximately 21 ft. [Courtesy Allis-Chalmers Mfg. Co.]

are shown in Fig. 10.9. The entire weight of the shaft and attached members must be included, but the shaft may be modified as shown by the dotted lines when the values for the moment of inertia are calculated. If it is expected that the critical speed is above the running speed, the assumptions can be made on the flexible side, and vice versa. If the critical speed cannot be determined exactly, it can be bracketed by this method. The stiffening effect of shrink fits is also difficult to evaluate.

Chapter 11

MANUAL LIFT TRUCK

11.1. *Introduction*

Lift trucks of the type shown in the following illustrations are designed for "in-between handling" with capacities ranging from 500 to 3000 lb. They are used when it is not economical to provide a skilled operator and motorized truck and are also used for certain types of work that cannot be performed by a large truck. The hand

Fig. 11.1. Foot-operated hydraulic lift truck, 750-lb capacity. [Courtesy Big Joe Mfg. Co.]

trucks are small enough to pass through narrow aisles, doorways, and into small elevators. They have a short turning radius which is sometimes required in the loading and unloading of box cars. Lift trucks similar to these are also made for battery operation.

11.2. *Design Details*

The accompanying illustrations show a representative group of lift trucks which can be studied for design details.

    A number of manufacturers provide multiple speed lifting units of which Fig. 11.6 is an example. The pump linkage is an inversion of the slider crank mechanism. The number 4 notch is used to lift

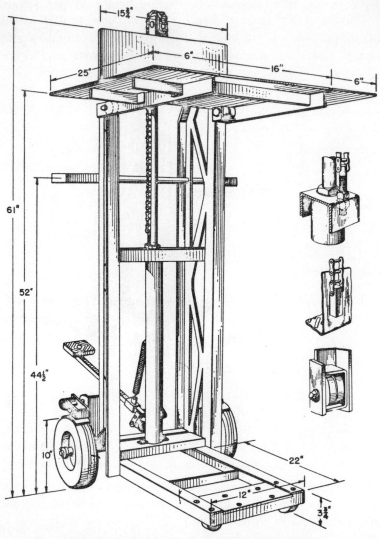

Fig. 11.2. Lift truck, dimensions and details.
[Courtesy Big Joe Mfg. Co.]

the empty platform while the number 1 notch is used for a full capacity load. Notches 2 and 3 are for intermediate loads.

One type of brake linkage is shown in Fig. 11.7. Here a four-bar linkage is used effectively as a toggle mechanism. Pressure on the foot brake causes the brake shoe to contact the wheel, and the toggle action provides the increasing mechanical advantage needed to apply the brake. This linkage can also be used to lock the brake in

Fig. 11.3. Hand-operated lift truck, 500-lb capacity.
[Courtesy Economy Engineering Co.]

the set position by allowing the toggle links to move past the dead center position, Fig. 11.7(b). The brake is released by pressing on the release pedal. A spring should be provided to hold the brake in the released position.

11.3. *Problem*

The statement of the problem will be furnished by the instructor.

Fig. 11.4. Foot-operated hydraulic lift truck, 1000-lb capacity. [Courtesy Safeway Industrial Equipment Co.]

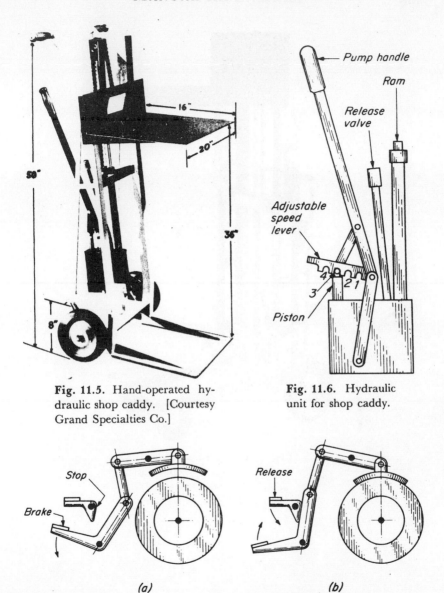

Fig. 11.5. Hand-operated hydraulic shop caddy. [Courtesy Grand Specialties Co.]

Fig. 11.6. Hydraulic unit for shop caddy.

Fig. 11.7. A type of rear-wheel brake showing (a) released position, (b) brake set position. The black circles are pivot points that are fixed relative to the frame.

Appendix

DESIGN DATA

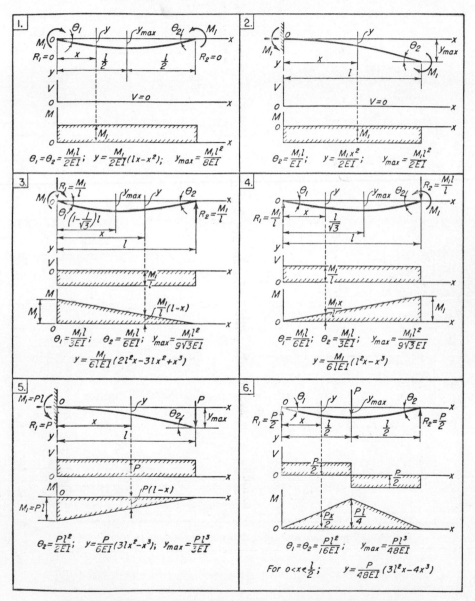

Fig. A.1. Shear, moment, and deflection in beams of uniform cross section. [From Spotts, *Design of Machine Elements*, Prentice-Hall, Inc., 2nd ed., 1953]

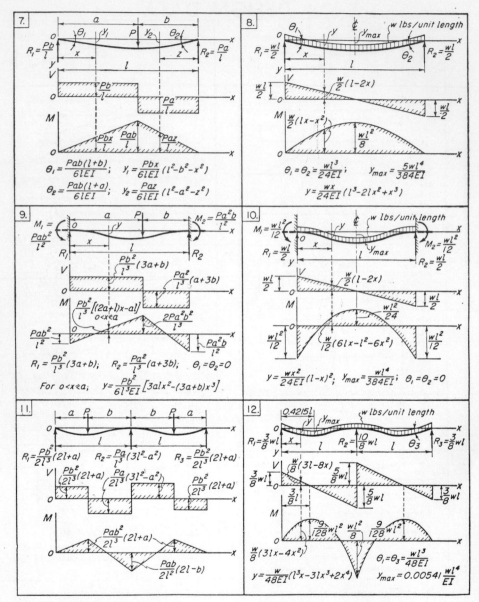

Fig. A.1. Shear, moment, and deflection in beams of uniform cross section.

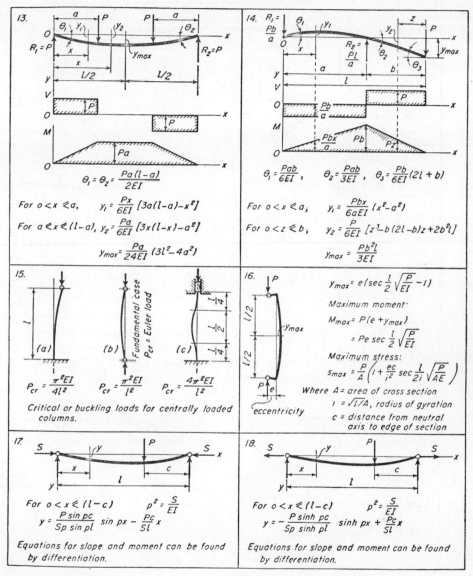

$$\theta_1 = \theta_2 = \frac{Pa(l-a)}{2EI}$$

For $0 < x \leqslant a$,　$y_1 = \frac{Px}{6EI}[3a(l-a)-x^2]$

For $a \leqslant x \leqslant (l-a)$, $y_2 = \frac{Pa}{6EI}[3x(l-x)-a^2]$

$$y_{max} = \frac{Pa}{24EI}(3l^2-4a^2)$$

$$\theta_1 = \frac{Pab}{6EI}, \qquad \theta_2 = \frac{Pab}{3EI}, \qquad \theta_3 = \frac{Pb}{6EI}(2l+b)$$

For $0 < x \leqslant a$;　$y_1 = \frac{Pbx}{6aEI}(x^2-a^2)$

For $0 < z \leqslant b$;　$y_2 = \frac{P}{6EI}[z^3-b(2l-b)z+2b^2l]$

$$y_{max} = \frac{Pb^2l}{3EI}$$

$$P_{cr} = \frac{\pi^2 EI}{4l^2} \qquad P_{cr} = \frac{\pi^2 EI}{l^2} \qquad P_{cr} = \frac{4\pi^2 EI}{l^2}$$

Critical or buckling loads for centrally loaded columns.

$$y_{max} = e\left(\sec \frac{1}{2}\sqrt{\frac{P}{EI}} - 1\right)$$

Maximum moment·

$$M_{max} = P(e+y_{max})$$

$$= Pe \sec \frac{1}{2}\sqrt{\frac{P}{EI}}$$

Maximum stress:

$$s_{max} = \frac{P}{A}\left(1+\frac{ec}{i^2}\sec\frac{1}{2i}\sqrt{\frac{P}{AE}}\right)$$

Where A = area of cross section

$i = \sqrt{I/A}$, radius of gyration

c = distance from neutral axis to edge of section

For $0 < x \leqslant (l-c)$　$p^2 = \frac{S}{EI}$

$$y = \frac{P\sin pc}{Sp \sin pl}\sin px - \frac{Pc}{Sl}x$$

Equations for slope and moment can be found by differentiation.

For $0 < x \leqslant (l-c)$　$p^2 = \frac{S}{EI}$

$$y = -\frac{P\sinh pc}{Sp \sinh pl}\sinh px + \frac{Pc}{Sl}x$$

Equations for slope and moment can be found by differentiation.

Fig. A.1. Shear, moment, and deflection in beams of uniform cross section.

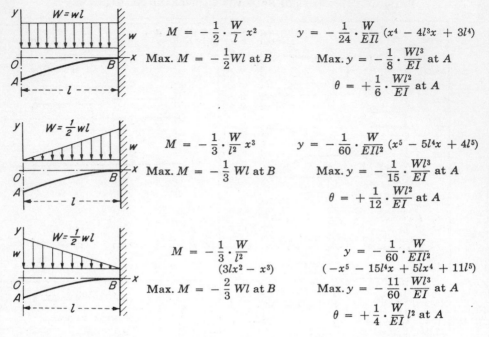

$$M = -\frac{1}{2} \cdot \frac{W}{l} x^2 \qquad y = -\frac{1}{24} \cdot \frac{W}{EIl} (x^4 - 4l^3x + 3l^4)$$

$$\text{Max. } M = -\frac{1}{2} Wl \text{ at } B \qquad \text{Max. } y = -\frac{1}{8} \cdot \frac{Wl^3}{EI} \text{ at } A$$

$$\theta = +\frac{1}{6} \cdot \frac{Wl^2}{EI} \text{ at } A$$

$$M = -\frac{1}{3} \cdot \frac{W}{l^2} x^3 \qquad y = -\frac{1}{60} \cdot \frac{W}{EIl^2} (x^5 - 5l^4x + 4l^5)$$

$$\text{Max. } M = -\frac{1}{3} Wl \text{ at } B \qquad \text{Max. } y = -\frac{1}{15} \cdot \frac{Wl^3}{EI} \text{ at } A$$

$$\theta = +\frac{1}{12} \cdot \frac{Wl^2}{EI} \text{ at } A$$

$$M = -\frac{1}{3} \cdot \frac{W}{l^2} \qquad y = -\frac{1}{60} \cdot \frac{W}{EIl^2}$$
$$(3lx^2 - x^3) \qquad (-x^5 - 15l^4x + 5lx^4 + 11l^5)$$

$$\text{Max. } M = -\frac{2}{3} Wl \text{ at } B \qquad \text{Max. } y = -\frac{11}{60} \cdot \frac{Wl^3}{EI} \text{ at } A$$

$$\theta = +\frac{1}{4} \cdot \frac{W}{EI} l^2 \text{ at } A$$

Fig. A.2. Moment and deflection formulas for beams of uniform cross section: $W =$ load (lb), $w =$ unit load (lb per linear in.). All deflections are in inches; θ is in radians, and $\tan \theta = \theta$. [After Roark, *Formulas for Stress and Strain*, McGraw-Hill Book Co., Inc.]

TABLE A.1
Physical Properties of Selected Carbon and Alloy Steels*

Steel	Condition	Tensile Strength	Yield Point	% El. in 2 in.	% Red. Area	BHN	Rock-well C	Machin-ability
1010	As-rolled	51,000	29,000	38	70	101		
	Cold-drawn	56,000	33,000	35	65	113		55%
1020	As-rolled	67,000	45,000	32	65	137		
	Cold-drawn	69,000	48,000	30	63	144		57%
1035	As-rolled	88,000	55,000	30	56	179	10	57%
	Cold-drawn	92,000	59,000	25	50	200	12	
1045	As-rolled	99,000	60,000	24	47	200	12	51%
	Cold-drawn	110,000	69,000	19	41	235	21	
	Annealed, 1450°F	90,000	54,000	28	54	170	8	57%
	Normalized, 1650°F	98,000	63,000	27	53	196	14	
1060	As-rolled	108,000	65,000	20	37	233	20	
	Annealed, 1450°F	95,000	59,000	24	51	187	12	
1095	Annealed	105,000	61,000	22	46	201	16	
	1 in. Rd. Oil\drawn 900°F	189,000	130,000	12	34	375	38	
	Q. 1450°F ∫drawn 1000°F	178,000	122,000	12	36	363	37	
1112	As-rolled	67,000	40,000	27	47	140		
	Cold-drawn	80,000	62,500	16	43	170	6	100%
1113 (X1112)	Cold-drawn	83,000	73,000	15	45	180	8	135%
1117 (X1314)	Hot-rolled	71,000	45,000	28	52	135		
	Cold-drawn	82,000	63,000	18	44	162		85%
1137 (X1335)	Hot-rolled	92,000	60,000	20	35	185	9	73%
	Cold-drawn	105,000	80,000	15	30	212	15	
T1330	As-rolled	110,000	72,000	21	57	229	21	
	Annealed, 1450°F	99,000	62,000	27	62	192	13	
2315	As-rolled	85,000	56,000	29	60	163		
	Cold-drawn	95,000	75,000	25	58	197	12	64%
2330	As-rolled	98,000	65,000	25	50	207	16	45%
	Cold-drawn	110,000	90,000	17	47	235	22	
	Annealed, 1450°F	80,000	50,000	30	60	157	4	61%
	Normalized, 1675°F	95,000	61,000	29	60	169	8	
3115	As-rolled	75,000	60,000	30	65	151		
	Cold-drawn	95,000	70,000	20	53	201	12	67%
	Annealed, 1500°F	71,000	62,000	36	70	146	1	
3140	As-rolled	110,000	75,000	23	52	223	20	36%
	Annealed	95,000	66,000	26	56	202	15	57%
	Normalized	111,000	78,000	21	51	248	21	
4119	As-rolled	91,000	52,000	28	62	179		
	Cold-drawn	97,000	63,000	21	51	207		
4140	Hot-rolled, annealed	90,000	63,000	27	58	187	12	61%
	Annealed and cold-drawn	114,000	90,000	18	50	241	23	
4615	As-rolled	82,000	55,000	30	61	167	4	
	Cold-drawn	98,000	70,000	18	55	203	14	64%
4640	Hot-rolled, annealed	100,000	87,000	21	50	201	12	
	Annealed and cold-drawn	126,000	97,000	14	39	269	27	

* Selected mainly from Hoyt, S. L., *Metal Data* (New York: Reinhold Publishing Corp., 1952).

TABLE A.1 (*cont.*)

Steel	Condition	Tensile Strength	Yield Point	% El. in 2 in.	% Red. Area	BHN	Rock-well C	Machin-ability
5140	As-rolled	115,000	75,000	20	58	223	20	
	Annealed, 1450°F	90,000	56,000	28	61	183		61%
	Normalized	110,000	70,000	22	60	212	18	
6115	As-rolled	83,000	64,000	30	68	174	9	
	Annealed, 1600°F	73,000	54,000	32	72	149	2	
6150	Hot-rolled, annealed	103,000	70,000	27	51	217	18	
	Annealed and cold-drawn	118,000	94,000	20	43	255	25	
	1 in. Rd. Oil ⎫drawn 900°F	202,000	196,000	12	44	421	44	
	Q. 1500°F ⎭drawn 1000°F	185,000	175,000	13	47	388	41	
AISI								
A8620	As-rolled	91,000	64,000	29	56	185		
	Annealed	76,000	51,000	32	63	155		
A8640	As-rolled	126,000	89,000	20	40	254		
	Annealed	95,000	63,000	26	55	193		55%
A8655	⅞ in. Rd. Oil Q. 1500–1550°F drawn 925–1000°F	183,000	161,000	15	48	379		
A8742	As-rolled	129,000	92,000	19	38	260		
	Annealed	97,000	65,000	25	54	196		51%
9255	As-rolled	132,000	90,000	19	40	269	27	
	Annealed, 1450°F	115,000	79,000	23	45	228	21	
	1 in. Rd. Oil ⎫drawn 900°F	207,000	186,000	11	27	415	42	
	Q. 1650°F ⎭drawn 1000°F	182,000	160,000	14	32	363	36	

TABLE A.2
STRENGTH OF GRAY CAST IRON*

Class No.	Tensile Strength, min.	Average Transverse Load†	Com-pressive Strength‡	Average Shear Strength	Modulus of Elasticity	BHN	Usual Min. Wall Thickness
20	20,000	1,800	80,000	32,500	11,600,000	110	⅛
25	25,000	2,000	100,000	34,000	14,200,000	140	⅛
30	30,000	2,200	110,000	41,000	14,500,000	170	¼
35	35,000	2,400	125,000	49,000	16,000,000	200	⅜
40	40,000	2,600	135,000	52,000	18,100,000	230	½
50	50,000	3,000	160,000	64,000	22,600,000	250	½
60	60,000	3,400	150,000	60,000	19,900,000	275	¾

* From Spotts, M. F., *Design of Machine Elements*, 2d ed. (Englewood Cliffs, N. J.: Prentice-Hall, Inc., 1953).
† Specimen 1.2 in. diameter, 18 in. supports, load at center.
‡ Subject to variations up to ±10%.

TABLE A.3
USES OF CARBON STEEL*

Carbon Range, %	Uses of Carbon Steel
0.05–0.10	Stampings, sheets, wire, rivets, welding stock, cold drawn parts.
0.10–0.20	Structural shapes, machine parts, carburized parts, screws.
0.20–0.30	Gears, shafting, levers, welded tubing, carburized parts.
0.30–0.40	Can be heat treated. Seamless tubing, shafts, connecting rods, crane hooks, axles.
0.40–0.50	Forgings, shafts, gears, studs.
0.60–0.70	Drop hammer dies, set screws, locomotive tires, lock washers, hard drawn spring wire.
0.70–0.80	Plow beams, cultivator disks, anvil faces, band saws, hammers, wrenches.
0.80–0.90	Plow shares, shovels, harrow blades, punches, rock drills, cold chisels, hand tools, music wire, leaf springs.
0.90–1.00	Springs, knives, axes, dies, hay rake teeth, harrow blades.
1.00–1.10	Drills, taps, milling cutters, kinves.
1.10–1.20	Drills, lathe tools.
1.20–1.30	Files, reamers, knives, metal cutting tools.
1.25–1.40	Razors, saws, wire-drawing dies, metal-cutting saws.

TABLE A.4
PROPERTIES OF MALLEABLE IRON AND MEEHANITE*

	Grade	Tensile Strength, min.	Yield Point, min.	Elong. % in 2 in.	Modulus of Elasticity
Malleable iron....	32510	50,000	32,500	10	25,000,000
ASTM 47-33.....	35018	53,000	35,000	18	25,000,000
Meehanite....... (Air furnace)		55,000	35,000	10	

*From Spotts, M. F., *Design of Machine Elements*, 2d ed. (Englewood Cliffs, N.J.: Prentice-Hall, Inc., 1953).

BRASS, BRONZE, AND MISCELLANEOUS WROUGHT COPPER ALLOYS*

No.	Alloy	Condition	Tensile Strength	Rockwell	Elong. % 2 in.
1	Copper	Bars, all sizes	A 37,000		25
		" 0.125–0.375 in.	H 50,000		8
		" 0.375–1.0 in.	H 45,000		10
2	Red Brass	Sheet & strip	½ H 51–61,000, H 63–72,000		
			Sp 78–86,000	56B, 72B, 82B	
3	Yellow Brass	" " "	½ H 56–66,000, H 71–81,000		
			Sp 90–99,000	60B, 79B, 89B	
4	" "	" " "	½ H 55–65,000, H 68–78,000		
			Sp 86–95,000	57B, 76B, 87B	
5	Commercial "Bronze"	Wire, 0.20–0.25 in.	½ H 56–67,000, H 70–79,000		
			Sp 84,000		
6	Brass Wire	" " " "	½ H 79–94,000, H102–117,000		
			Sp 120,000		
7	F. C. Leaded Brass	Bars, 1 in. & under	A 48,000, YS 20,000		20
		" 1 in.–2 in.	A 44,000, YS 18,000		25
		" 0.50 & under	½ H 57,000, YS 25,000		7
		" 0.50–1.0 in.	½ H 55,000, YS 25,000		15
8	Naval Brass	Bars, 1 in. & under	A 54,000, YS 20,000		30
		" 1 in.–2.5 in.	A 52,000, YS 20,000		30
		" 0.50 & under	½ H 60,000, YS 27,000		22
		" 0.50–1.0 in.	½ H 60,000, YS 27,000		25
9	Phosphor Bronze	Wire, 0.025 & under	Sp 145,000		
		" 0.025–0.0625	Sp 135,000		
		" 0.125–0.250	Sp 125,000		
10	F. C. Phosphor Bronze	Rounds, 0.25–0.50	H 60,000		10
		" 0.50–1.0	H 55,000		12
11	Manganese Bronze	Bars, 2.5 in. & under	½ H 70,000, YS 35,000		20
		" " " "	H 78,000, YS 55,000		15
12	Muntz Metal	Tube plates	50,000, YS 20,000		35
13	Aluminum Bronze	Bars, 0.50 & under	80,000, YS 40,000		9
		" over 1 in.	72,000, YS 35,000		12
14	Beryllium Copper	Rods & bars	A 80,000 max., H 95,000	80B–90B	35, 10
		" " " H.T.	A 150,000, YS 90,000	33C	5
		" " " "	H 180,000, YS 95,000	38C	1
15	18% Ni Silver	Rods 0.10–0.50 in.	H 105–120,000,		
			Sp 118–140,000		
16	Monel Metal	Cold drawn bars	A 70–85,000, YS 30–40,000	BHN110– 140	35–50

No.	ASTM Specification	Alloy	Cu	Sn	Zn	Others
1	B133–49T	Copper	99.90	....	....	
2	B36–49T, Alloy 3	Red Brass	85	....	15	
3	B36–49T, Alloy 6	Yellow Brass	70	....	30	
4	B36–49T, Alloy 8	Yellow Brass	65	....	35	
5	B134–49, Alloy 2	Commercial "Bronze"	90	....	10	
6	B134–49, Alloy 7	Brass Wire	65	....	35	
7	B16–49	F.C. Leaded Brass	60.0–63.0	....	remainder	Pb 2.50–3.70
8	B21–49T, Alloy A & B	Naval Brass	59.0–62.0	0.5–1.0	remainder[a]	
9	B159–49T, Alloy A	Phosphor-Bronze Wire	remainder	3.5–5.8	0.30	P 0.03–0.35
10	B139–49T, Alloy B2	F.C. Phosphor Bronze	remainder	3.5–4.5	1.5–4.5	P 0.01–0.50[b]
11	B138–49, Alloy A	Manganese Bronze	58.5	1.0	39.0	Mn 0.1
12	B171–49	Muntz Metal	58.0–61.0	0.25 max.	remainder	Pb 0.35–0.90
13	B150–49T, Alloy I	Aluminum Bronze	80.0–93.0	0.60 max.	....	Al 6.5–11.0[c]
14	B120–41T	Beryllium Copper	remainder	....	....	Be 1.90–2.20
15	B151–44T, Alloy B	18% Ni Silver	53.5–56.5	Ni 17–19.5	remainder	Mn 0.5 max.
16		Monel Metal	30	Ni 67	Fe 1.4	Mn 1.0

F.C., free cutting; A, annealed or soft; ½ H, half hard; H, hard; Sp., spring; YS, yield strength; H.T., heat treated.

* From Spotts, M. F., *Design of Machine Elements*, 2d ed. (Englewood Cliffs, N. J.: Prentice-Hall, Inc., 1953).

[a] Pb, Grade A, 0.20 max.; Grade B, 0.4–1.0.

[b] Pb 3.5–4.5.

[c] Fe 4.0 max., Ni 1.0 max., Si 2.25, Mn 1.5, F.C., free cutting.

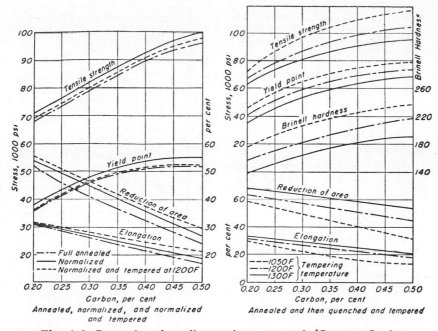

Fig. A.3. Properties of medium-carbon cast steel. [Courtesy Steel Founders Society of America]

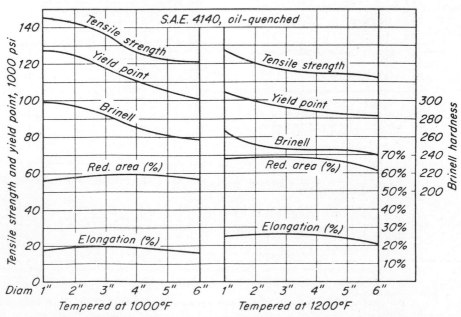

Fig. A.4. Properties of SAE 4140 steel, oil-quenched. [Courtesy Republic Steel Corp.]

149

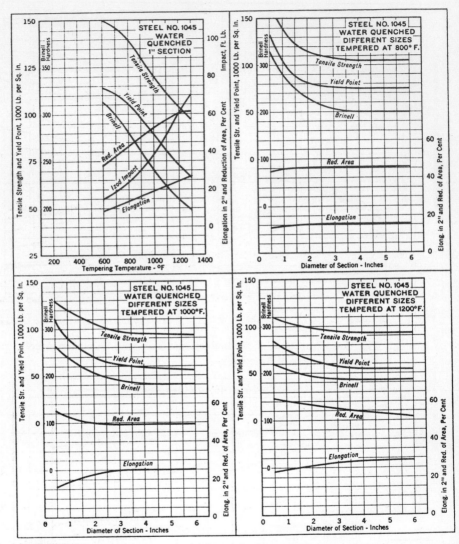

In section ½″ to 2″ incl., quenched from 1475/1525° F.; over 2″ to 4″ incl., from 1500/1550° F.; over 4″, from 1525/1575° F.

Fig. A.5. Properties of water-quenched and tempered carbon steel 1045 in different sizes. [Courtesy International Nickel Co.]

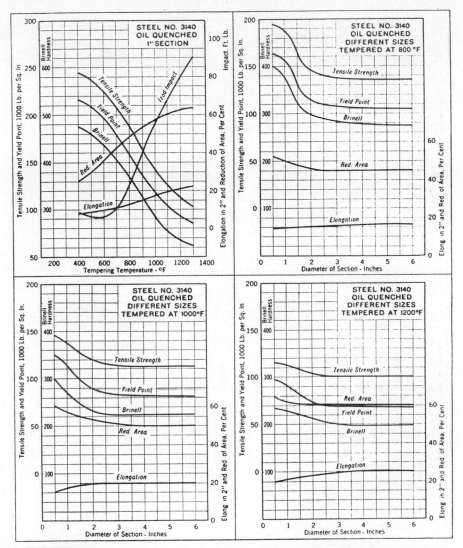

In sections ½″ to 2″ incl., quenched from 1475/1525° F.; over 2″ to 4″ incl., from 1500/1550° F.; over 4″, from 1525/1575° F.

Fig. A.6. Properties of oil-quenched and tempered nickel-chromium steel 3140 in different sizes. [Courtesy International Nickel Co.]

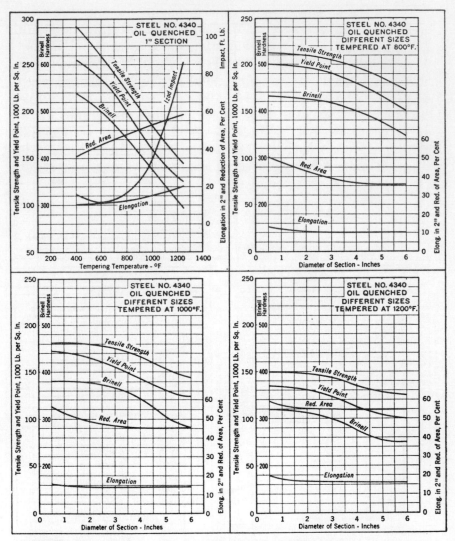

In sections ½" to 2" incl., quenched from 1500/1550° F.; over 2" to 4" incl., from 1525/1575° F.; over 4", from 1550/1600° F.

Fig. A.7. Properties of oil-quenched and tempered nickel-chromium-molybdenum steel 4340 in different sizes. [Courtesy International Nickel Co.]

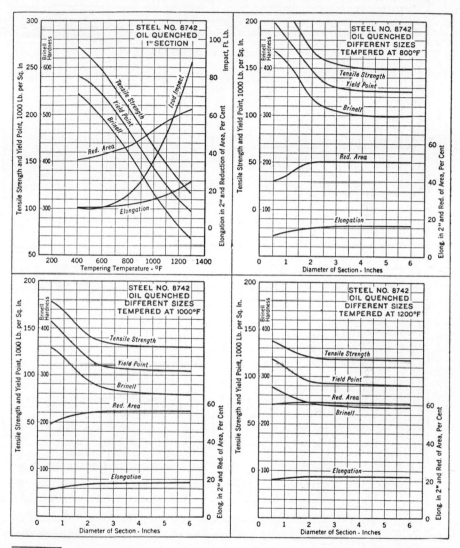

In sections ½″ to 2″ incl., quenched from 1500/1550° F.; over 2″ to 4″ incl., from 1525/1575° F.; over 4″, from 1550/1600° F

Fig. A.8. Properties of oil-quenched and tempered nickel-chromium-molybdenum steel 8742 in different sizes. [Courtesy International Nickel Co.]

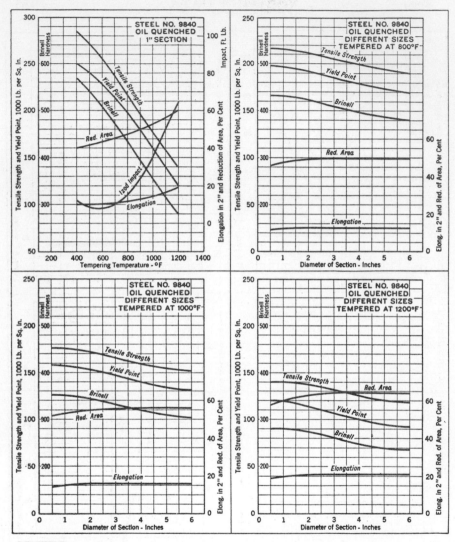

In sections ½″ to 2″ incl., quenched from 1525/1575° F.; over 2″ to 4″ incl., from 1550/1575° F.; over 4″, from 1575/1625° F.

Fig. A.9. Properties of oil-quenched and tempered nickel-chromium-molybdenum steel 9840 in different sizes. [Courtesy International Nickel Co.]

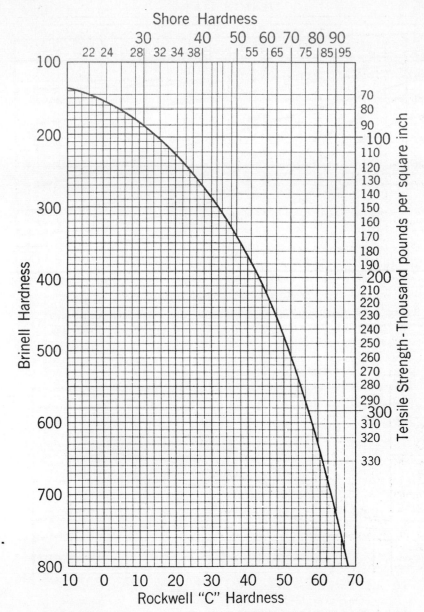

Fig. A.10. Relationship between tensile strength of steel and hardness by various designations. [Courtesy International Nickel Co.]

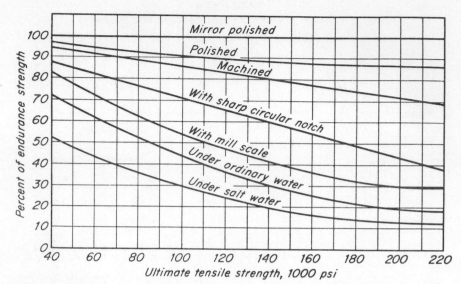

Fig. A.11. Endurance strength reduction due to surface conditions. [After Karpov, "Fatigue Problems in Structural Design," *Metals and Alloys*, December 1939]

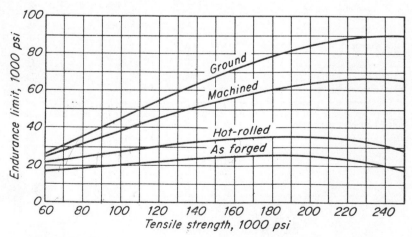

Fig. A.12. Endurance limit versus tensile strength. [After Noll and Lipson, "Allowable Working Stresses," *Proc. Exp. Stress Anal.*, Vol. III, No. 2, 1946]

TABLE A.6
FATIGUE STRESS CONCENTRATION FACTORS FOR KEYWAYS*

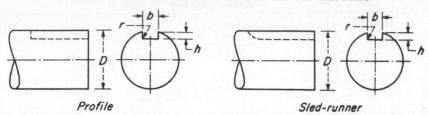

Profile   Sled-runner

Kind of Keyway	Annealed		Quenched and Drawn	
	Bending	Torsion	Bending	Torsion
Profile.............	1.6	1.3	2.0	1.6
Sled-runner........	1.3	1.3	1.6	1.6

*The values are the average of the existing fatigue values for profile and sled-runner type keyways. The values will hold true for keyways which have ratios $b = D/4$, $h = D/8$, $D = 0.4$ to 2.0 in. and r not to exceed 0.015 in.

From Lipson, Noll, and Clock, *Stress and Strength of Manufactured Parts* (New York: McGraw-Hill Book Co., Inc., 1950).

TABLE A.7
FATIGUE STRESS CONCENTRATION FACTORS FOR SCREW THREADS*

Kind of Thread	Annealed		Quenched and Drawn	
	Rolled	Cut	Rolled	Cut
U.S. Standard......	2.2	2.8	3.0	3.8
Whitworth..........	1.4	1.8	2.6	3.3
Dardalet...........	1.8	2.3	2.6	3.3
Aero Stud.........	1.2	1.5	2.3	2.8

*The factors are the average of the existing fatigue values in bending and tension.

From Lipson, Noll, and Clock, *Stress and Strength of Manufactured Parts* (New York: McGraw-Hill Book Co., Inc., 1950).

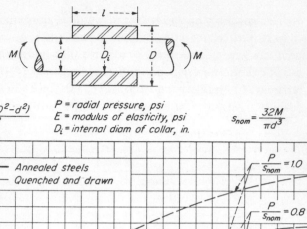

$$P = \frac{(E)(d-D_i)(D^2-d^2)}{2dD^2}$$

P = radial pressure, psi
E = modulus of elasticity, psi
D_i = internal diam of collar, in.

$$s_{nom} = \frac{32M}{\pi d^3}$$

Fig. A.13. Stress concentration factor K for solid circular shaft with plane press fit, bending. [After Lipson, Noll, and Clock, *Stress and Strength of Manufactured Parts*, McGraw-Hill Book Co., Inc.]

Stress Concentration Factors

Figures A.14 through A.32 show stress concentration factors for various members under various conditions. These graphs are redrawn, by permission, from R. E. Peterson, *Stress Concentration Design Factors*, John Wiley & Sons, Inc., 1953.

K_t = stress concentration factor for normal stress, s_{max}/s_{nom}.
   Used for: brittle materials; ductile materials subjected to a static load, when it is desirable to use a stress concentration factor; flat members made of a ductile material, when subjected to a variable, uniaxial loading.

K'_t = combined factor, taking account of stress concentration (normal stress) and Mises criterion for failure. Used for round members made from ductile material subjected to variable loading.

K_{ts} = stress concentration factor for shear stress, $(s_s)_{max}/(s_s)_{nom}$. K_{ts} and K'_{ts} are the same.

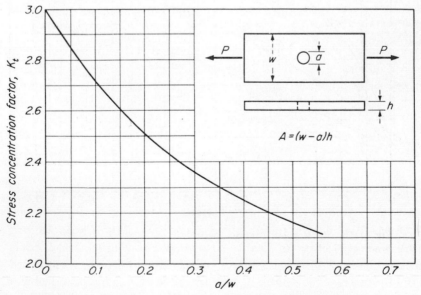

Fig. A.14. Stress concentration factor K_t for plate with hole, in tension.

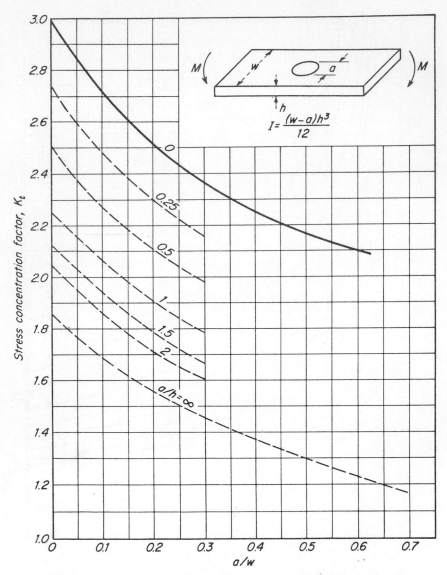

Fig. A.15. Stress concentration factor K_t for plate with hole, in bending.

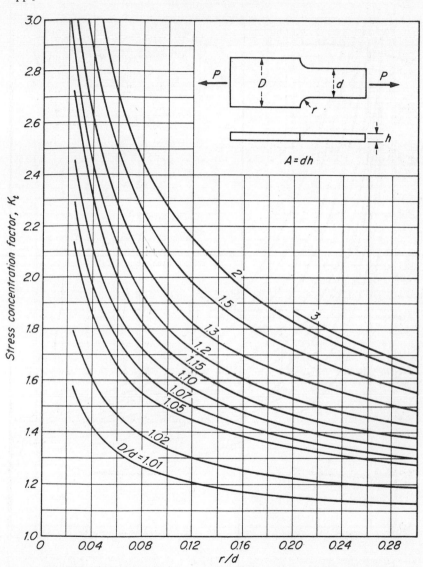

Fig. A.16. Stress concentration factor K_t for stepped bar in tension.

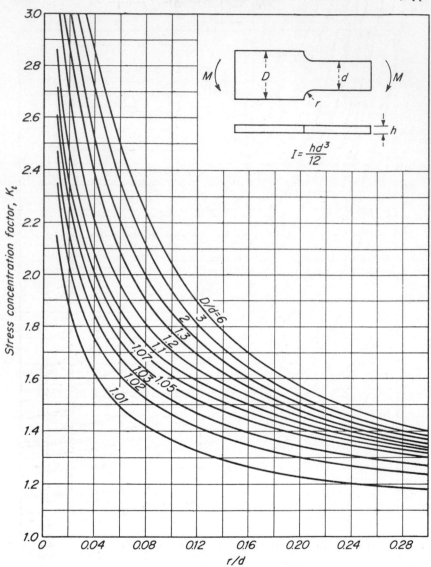

Fig. A.17. Stress concentration factor K_t for stepped bar in bending.

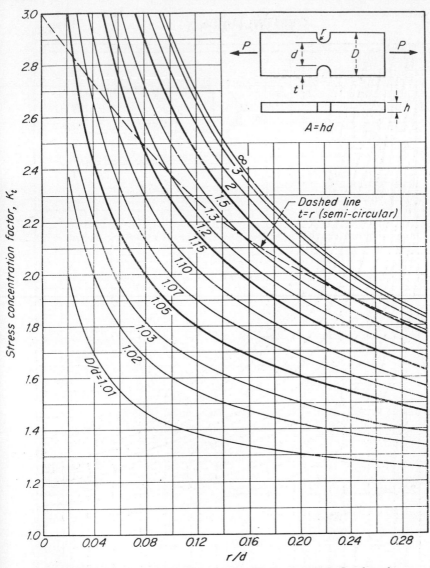

Fig. A.18. Stress concentration factor K_t for notched flat bar in tension.

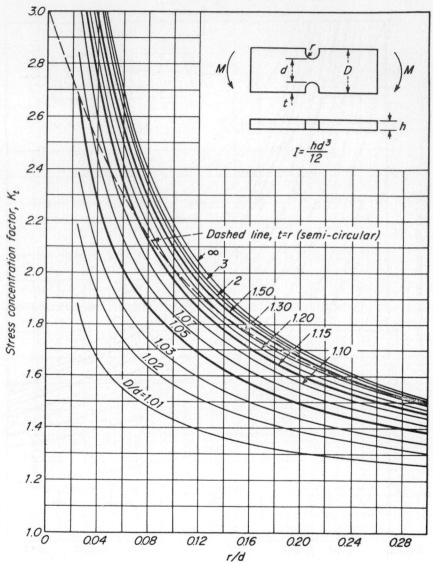

Fig. A.19. Stress concentration factor K_t for notched flat bar in bending.

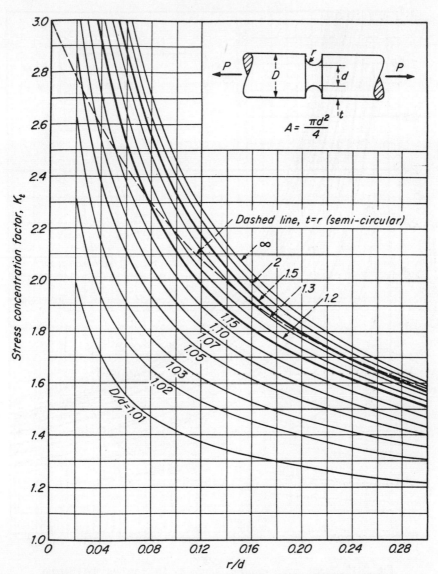

Fig. A.20. Stress concentration factor K_t for grooved shaft in tension.

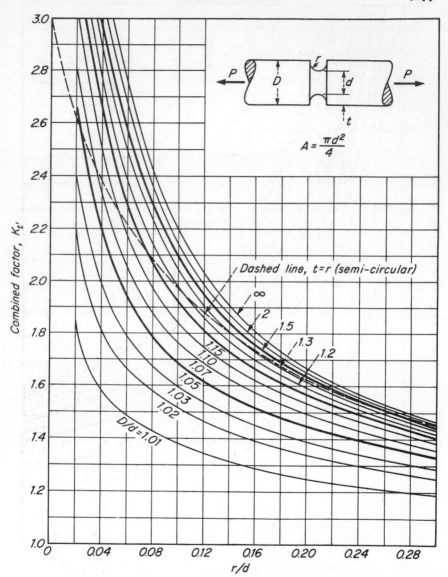

Fig. A.21. Combined factor K'_t for grooved shaft in tension.

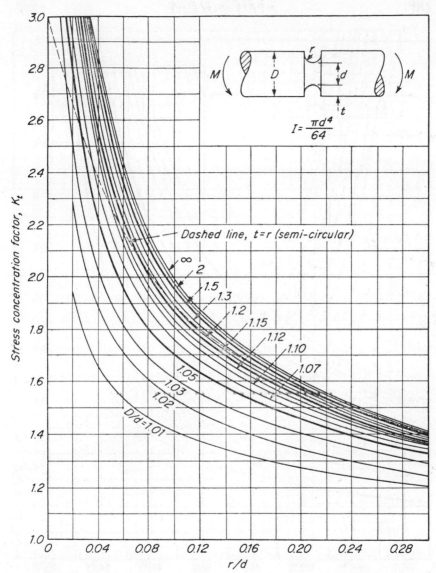

Fig. A.22. Stress concentration factor K_t for grooved shaft in bending.

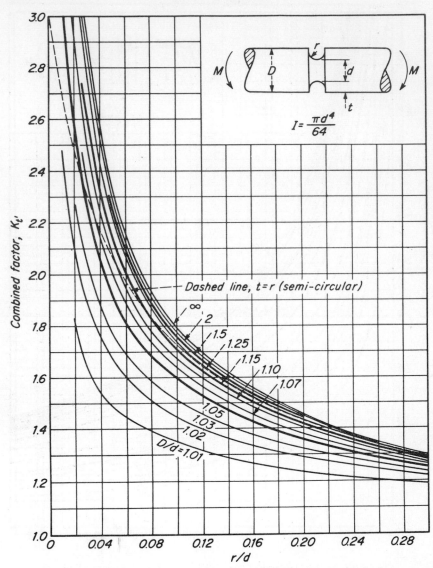

Fig. A.23. Combined factor K'_t for grooved shaft in bending.

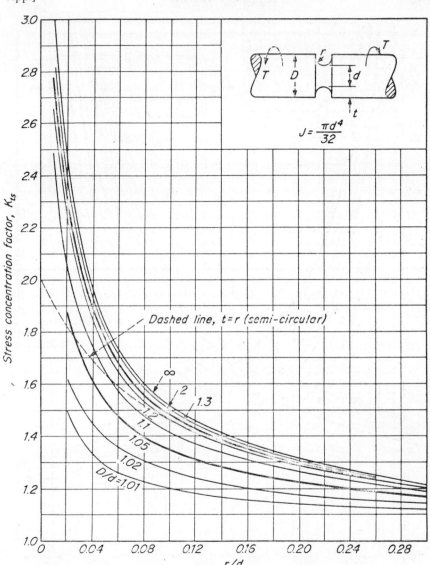

Fig. A.24. Stress concentration factor K_{ts} for grooved shaft in torsion.

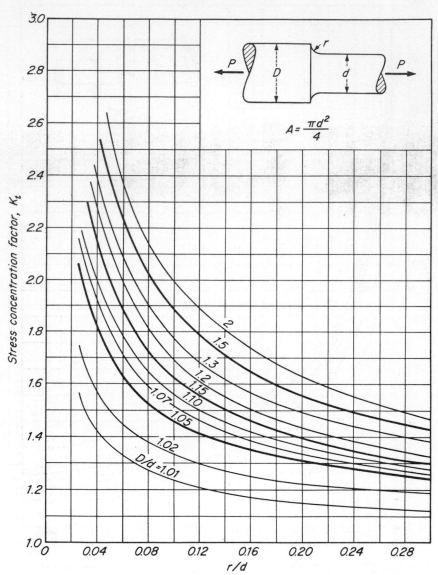

Fig. A.25. Stress concentration factor K_t for stepped shaft in tension.

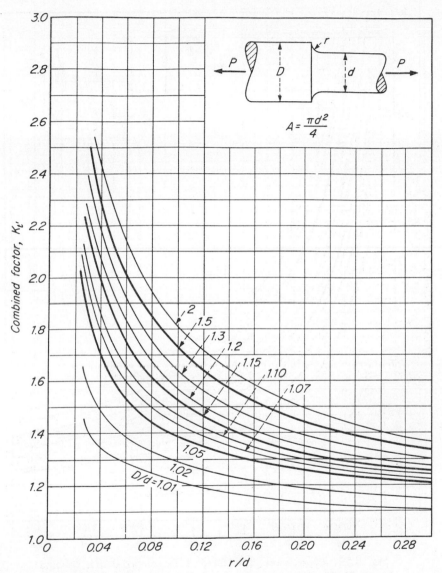

Fig. A.26. Combined factor K'_t for stepped shaft in tension.

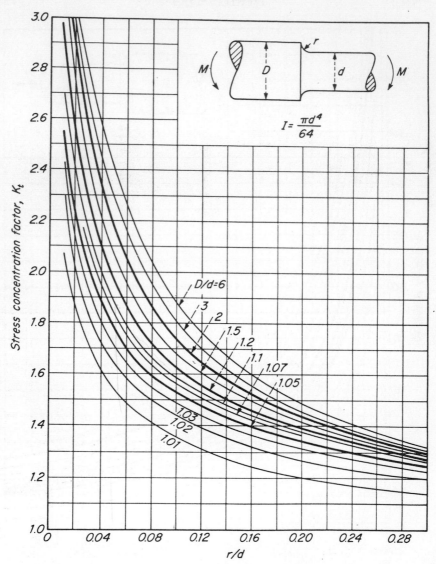

Fig. A.27. Stress concentration factor K_t for stepped shaft in bending.

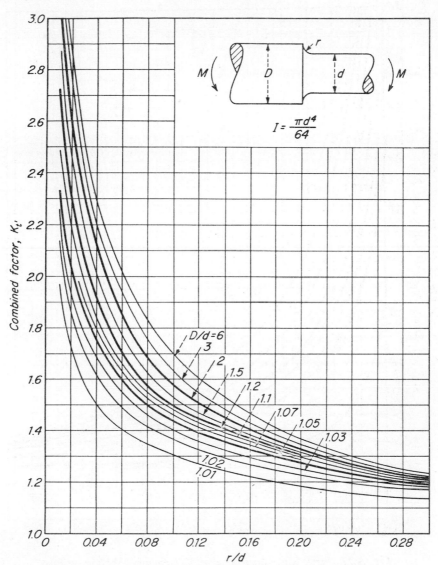

Fig. A.28. Combined factor K'_t for stepped shaft in bending.

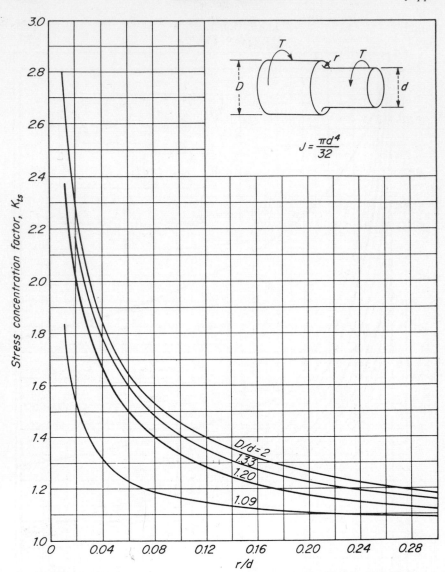

Fig. A.29. Stress concentration factor K_{ts} for stepped shaft in torsion.

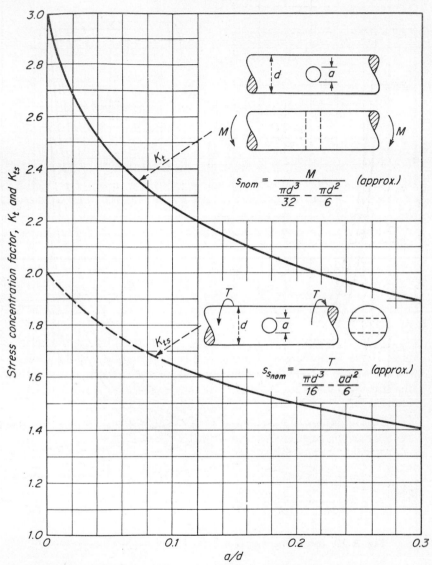

Fig. A.30. Stress concentration factors K_t and K_{ts} for shaft with transverse hole in bending and torsion.

Springs[1]

The stress and deflection equations for helical springs are,

$$s_s = K\frac{8PD}{\pi d^3} = K\frac{8PC}{\pi D^2}, \quad \delta = \frac{8PD^3 n}{Gd^4} = \frac{8PC^3 n}{Gd}$$

where P = axial load, D = mean coil diameter, d = wire diameter, C = spring index D/d, n = number of active coils, K = stress factor, Fig. A.31.

SAE 6150 steel is a commonly used spring material. Allowable working stresses are given in Table A.8.

For the cantilever spring, Fig. A.35, the stress and deflection equations are

$$s = K_2\frac{3\delta Eh}{L^2}, \quad \delta = C_1\frac{QL^3}{12EI}$$

where $I = bh^3/12$, and K_2 and C_1 are factors that are plotted in Figs. A.33 and A.34.

When the width of the spring is large compared with the thickness, say 8 or 10 to 1, anticlastic deformation is appreciable and the deflection obtained from the above equation should be multiplied by $(1 - \mu^2)$ while the stress is divided by $(1 - \mu^2)$, where μ = Poisson's ratio.

---

[1] Most of this material is based on A. M. Wahl, *Mechanical Springs* (Cleveland: Penton Publishing Co., 1944).

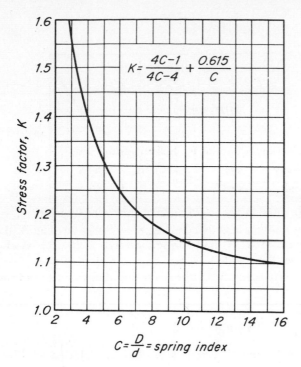

$$K = \frac{4C-1}{4C-4} + \frac{0.615}{C}$$

Fig. A.31. Wahl stress factor K for helical springs.

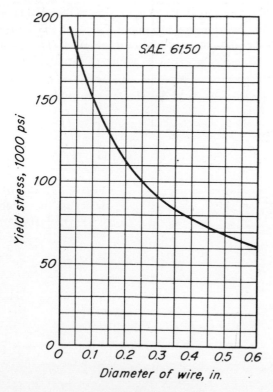

Fig. A.32. Torsional elastic limit for SAE 6150 spring wire.

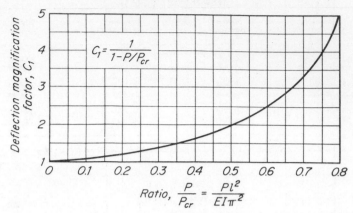

Fig. A.33. Factor C_1 for cantilever spring under combined loading.

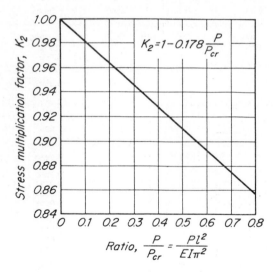

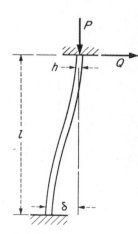

Fig. A.34. Factor K_2 for cantilever spring subjected to combined loading.

Fig. A.35. Cantilever subjected to combined axial and transverse loading.

TABLE A.8
Working Stresses, Shear, psi, for SAE 6150 Oil-tempered hot-wound Springs heat-treated after Forming*

Wire Diameter, in.	Severe Service	Average Service	Light Service
Up to 0.085	60,000	75,000	93,000
0.085–0.185	55,000	69,000	85,000
0.185–0.320	48,000	60,000	74,000
0.320–0.530	42,000	52,000	65,000
0.530–0.970	36,000	45,000	56,000
0.970–1.5	32,000	40,000	50,000

*These working stresses should be used in equations with the stress factor K.

TABLE A.9
Wire Sizes

Washburn & Moen Wire Gauge No.	Fraction of Inch	Decimal of Inch	Washburn & Moen Wire Gauge No.	Fraction of Inch	Decimal of Inch
	½*	0.5000		3⁄32	0.09375
7–0		0.490	13		0.092
	15⁄32	0.46875	14		0.080
6–0		0.462	15		0.072
	7⁄16	0.4375	16	1⁄16	0.0625
5–0		0.431	17		0.054
	13⁄32	0.40625	18		0.047
4–0		0.394	19		0.041
	3⁄8	0.3750	20		0.035
3–0		0.3629	21		0.032
	11⁄32	0.34375		1⁄32	0.03125
2–0		0.331	22		0.0286
	5⁄16	0.3125	23		0.0258
0		0.307	24		0.0230
1		0.283	25		0.0204
	9⁄32	0.28125	26		0.0181
2		0.263	27		0.0173
	¼	0.250	28		0.0162
3		0.244		1⁄64	0.0156
4		0.225	29		0.0150
	7⁄32	0.21875	30		0.0140
5		0.207	31		0.0132
6		0.192	32		0.0128
	3⁄16	0.1875	33		0.0118
7		0.177	34		0.0104
8		0.162	35		0.0095
	5⁄32	0.15625	36		0.009
9		0.148	37		0.0085
10		0.135	38		0.008
	⅛	0.125	39		0.0075
11		0.120	40		0.007
12		0.105	41		0.0066
			42		0.0062

*Between ½ and 1 in., wire sizes vary by 1⁄32-in. intervals.

TABLE A.10
UNIFIED AND AMERICAN SCREW-THREAD SIZES*

Size		Coarse Threads				Fine Threads			
		Threads per in.	Minor Diam, in.	Root Area, sq in.	Stress Area, sq in.	Threads per in.	Minor Diam, in.	Root Area, sq in.	Stress Area, sq in.
0		..	......	......	......	80	0.0447	0.0015	0.0018
1	(0.073)	64	0.0538	0.0022	0.0026	72	0.0560	0.0024	0.0027
2	(0.086)	56	0.0641	0.0031	0.0036	64	0.0668	0.0034	0.0039
3	(0.099)	48	0.0734	0.0041	0.0048	56	0.0771	0.0045	0.0052
4	(0.112)	40	0.0813	0.0050	0.0060	48	0.0864	0.0057	0.0065
5	(0.125)	40	0.0943	0.0067	0.0079	44	0.0971	0.0072	0.0082
6	(0.138)	32	0.0997	0.0075	0.0090	40	0.1073	0.0087	0.0101
8	(0.164)	32	0.1257	0.0120	0.0139	36	0.1299	0.0128	0.0146
10	(0.190)	24	0.1389	0.0145	0.0174	32	0.1517	0.0175	0.0199
12	(0.216)	24	0.1649	0.0206	0.0240	28	0.1722	0.0226	0.0257
¼	U	20	0.1887	0.0269	0.0317	28	0.2062	0.0326	0.0362
⁵⁄₁₆	U	18	0.2443	0.0454	0.0522	24	0.2614	0.0524	0.0579
⅜	U	16	0.2983	0.0678	0.0773	24	0.3239	0.0809	0.0876
⁷⁄₁₆	U	14	0.3499	0.0933	0.1060	20	0.3762	0.1090	0.1185
½		13	0.4056	0.1257	0.1416	..	......	......	......
½	U	12	0.3978	0.1205	0.1374	20	0.4387	0.1486	0.1597
⁹⁄₁₆	U	12	0.4603	0.1620	0.1816	18	0.4943	0.1888	0.2026
⅝	U	11	0.5135	0.2018	0.2256	18	0.5568	0.2400	0.2555
¾	U	10	0.6273	0.3020	0.3340	16	0.6733	0.3513	0.3724
⅞	U	9	0.7387	0.4193	0.4612	14	0.7874	0.4805	0.5088
1	U	8	0.8466	0.5510	0.6051	12	0.8978	0.6245	0.6624
1⅛	U	7	0.9497	0.6931	0.7627	12	1.0228	0.8118	0.8549
1¼	U	7	1.0747	0.8898	0.9684	12	1.1478	1.0237	1.0721
1⅜	U	6	1.1705	1.0541	1.1538	12	1.2728	1.2602	1.3137
1½	U	6	1.2955	1.2938	1.4041	12	1.3978	1.5212	1.5799
1¾	U	5	1.5046	1.7441	1.8983				
2	U	4½	1.7274	2.3001	2.4971				
2¼	U	4½	1.9774	3.0212	3.2464				
2½	U	4	2.1933	3.7161	3.9976				
2¾	U	4	2.4433	4.6194	4.9326				
3	U	4	2.6933	5.6209	5.9659				
3¼	U	4	2.9433	6.7205	7.0992				
3½	U	4	3.1933	7.9183	8.3268				
3¾	U	4	3.4433	9.2143	9.6546				
4	U	4	3.6933	10.6084	11.0805				

* The unified threads are indicated by U.　The stress area is the mean of the average pitch diameter area and the average minor diameter area for class 3A tolerances.　(See *Unified and American Screw Threads*, ASA Standard B 1.1–1949.)

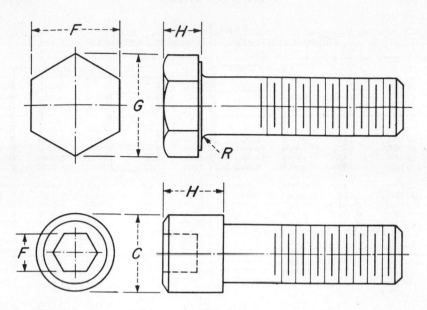

TABLE A.11
REGULAR SEMIFINISHED HEXAGON BOLTS* AND SOCKET-HEAD CAPSCREWS†

Nominal Size	Hexagon Head				Socket Head		
	F Max.	G Max.	H Nominal	R Max.	C Max.	H Max.	F
¼	⁷⁄₁₆	0.505	⁵⁄₃₂	0.031	⅜	¼	0.1895
⁵⁄₁₆	½	0.577	¹³⁄₆₄	0.031	⁷⁄₁₆	⁷⁄₁₆	0.2207
⅜	⁹⁄₁₆	0.650	¹⁵⁄₆₄	0.031	⁹⁄₁₆	⁹⁄₁₆	0.3155
⁷⁄₁₆	⅝	0.722	⁹⁄₃₂	0.031	⅝	⅝	0.3155
½	¾	0.866	⁵⁄₁₆	0.031	¾	¾	0.3780
⅝	¹⁵⁄₁₆	1.083	²⁵⁄₆₄	0.062	⅞	⅞	0.5030
¾	1 ⅛	1.299	¹⁵⁄₃₂	0.062	1	1	0.5655
⅞	1 ⁵⁄₁₆	1.516	³⁵⁄₆₄	0.062	1 ⅛	1 ⅛	0.5655
1	1 ½	1.732	³⁹⁄₆₄	0.093	1 ⁵⁄₁₆	1 ⁵⁄₁₆	0.6290
1 ⅛	1 ¹¹⁄₁₆	1.949	¹¹⁄₁₆	0.093	1 ½	1 ½	0.7540
1 ¼	1 ⅞	2.165	²⁵⁄₃₂	0.093	1 ¾	1 ¾	0.7540
1 ⅜	2 ¹⁄₁₆	2.382	²⁷⁄₃₂	0.093	1 ⅞	1 ⅞	0.7540
1 ½	2 ¼	2.598	¹⁵⁄₁₆	0.093	2	2	1.0040
1 ¾	2 ⅝	3.031	1 ³⁄₃₂	0.125			
2	3	3.464	1 ⁷⁄₃₂	0.125			
2 ¼	3 ⅜	3.897	1 ⅜	0.188			
2 ½	3 ¾	4.330	1 ¹⁷⁄₃₂	0.188			
2 ¾	4 ⅛	4.763	1 ¹¹⁄₁₆	0.188			
3	4 ½	5.196	1 ⅞	0.188			

* From ASA Standard B 18.2-1955.
† From ASA Standard B 18.3-1947.

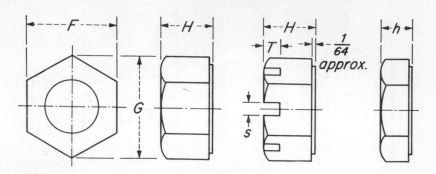

TABLE A.12
FINISHED HEXAGON, HEXAGON JAM, AND HEXAGON SLOTTED NUTS*

Nominal Size	Regular, Jam, Slotted		Regular, Slotted	Jam	Slotted	
	F Max.	G Max.	H Nominal	h Nominal	S	T
$\frac{1}{4}$	$\frac{7}{16}$	0.505	$\frac{7}{32}$	$\frac{5}{32}$	0.078	0.094
$\frac{5}{16}$	$\frac{1}{2}$	0.577	$\frac{17}{64}$	$\frac{3}{16}$	0.094	0.094
$\frac{3}{8}$	$\frac{9}{16}$	0.650	$\frac{21}{64}$	$\frac{7}{32}$	0.125	0.125
$\frac{7}{16}$	$\frac{11}{16}$	0.794	$\frac{3}{8}$	$\frac{1}{4}$	0.125	0.156
$\frac{1}{2}$	$\frac{3}{4}$	0.866	$\frac{7}{16}$	$\frac{5}{16}$	0.156	0.156
$\frac{5}{8}$	$\frac{15}{16}$	1.083	$\frac{35}{64}$	$\frac{3}{8}$	0.188	0.219
$\frac{3}{4}$	$1\frac{1}{8}$	1.299	$\frac{41}{64}$	$\frac{27}{64}$	0.188	0.250
$\frac{7}{8}$	$1\frac{5}{16}$	1.516	$\frac{3}{4}$	$\frac{31}{64}$	0.188	0.250
1	$1\frac{1}{2}$	1.732	$\frac{55}{64}$	$\frac{35}{64}$	0.250	0.281
$1\frac{1}{8}$	$1\frac{11}{16}$	1.949	$\frac{31}{32}$	$\frac{39}{64}$	0.250	0.344
$1\frac{1}{4}$	$1\frac{7}{8}$	2.165	$1\frac{1}{16}$	$\frac{23}{32}$	0.312	0.375
$1\frac{3}{8}$	$2\frac{1}{16}$	2.382	$1\frac{11}{64}$	$\frac{25}{32}$	0.312	0.375
$1\frac{1}{2}$	$2\frac{1}{4}$	2.598	$1\frac{9}{32}$	$\frac{27}{32}$	0.375	0.438
$1\frac{3}{4}$	$2\frac{5}{8}$	3.031	$1\frac{1}{2}$	$\frac{31}{32}$	0.438	0.500
2	3	3.464	$1\frac{23}{32}$	$1\frac{3}{32}$	0.438	0.562
$2\frac{1}{4}$	$3\frac{3}{8}$	3.897	$1\frac{59}{64}$	$1\frac{13}{64}$	0.438	0.562
$2\frac{1}{2}$	$3\frac{3}{4}$	4.330	$2\frac{9}{64}$	$1\frac{29}{64}$	0.562	0.688
$2\frac{3}{4}$	$4\frac{1}{8}$	4.763	$2\frac{23}{64}$	$1\frac{1}{2}$	0.562	0.688
3	$4\frac{1}{2}$	5.196	$2\frac{37}{64}$	$1\frac{45}{64}$	0.562	0.750

* From ASA Standard B 18.2-1955.

TABLE A.13
VALUES OF J/c AND I/c FOR VARIOUS DIAMETERS

Values of $\pi d^3/16$ (d = diameter of shaft)

d	0	1/16	1/8	3/16	1/4	5/16	3/8	7/16	1/2	9/16	5/8	11/16	3/4	13/16	7/8	15/16	d
0	0	0.000048	0.00038	0.0013	0.0031	0.006	0.0104	0.0164	0.0245	0.0349	0.0479	0.0638	0.0828	0.1053	0.1315	0.1618	0
1	0.196	0.236	0.280	0.329	0.384	0.444	0.510	0.583	0.663	0.749	0.843	0.944	1.052	1.169	1.294	1.428	1
2	1.571	1.723	1.884	2.055	2.236	2.428	2.630	2.843	3.068	3.304	3.551	3.811	4.083	4.368	4.666	4.977	2
3	5.301	5.639	5.992	6.359	6.740	7.136	7.548	7.975	8.416	8.877	9.352	9.845	10.35	10.88	11.42	11.99	3
4	12.57	13.16	13.78	14.42	15.07	15.75	16.44	17.16	17.89	18.65	19.42	20.22	21.04	21.88	22.75	23.63	4
5	24.54	25.47	26.43	27.41	28.41	29.44	30.49	31.56	32.66	33.79	34.94	36.12	37.33	38.56	39.82	41.10	5
6	42.41	43.75	45.12	46.51	47.93	49.39	50.87	52.38	53.92	55.49	57.09	58.72	60.38	62.08	63.80	65.56	6
7	67.35		71.02		74.82		78.76		82.83		87.04		91.39		95.89		7
8	100.5		105.3		110.3		115.3		120.6		126.0		131.5		137.3		8
9	143.1		149.2		155.4		161.8		168.3		175.1		182.0		189.1		9
10	196.4		203.8		211.4		219.3		227.3		235.5		243.9		252.5		10
11	261.3		270.3		279.6		289.0		298.6		308.5		318.5		328.8		11
12	339.3		350.0		361.0		372.1		383.5		395.1		407.0		419.1		12
13	431.4		443.9		456.8		469.8		483.1		496.6		510.4		524.5		13
14	538.8		553.3		568.2		583.3		598.6		614.2		630.1		646.3		14
15	662.7		679.4		696.4		713.6		731.2		749.0		767.1		785.6		15

Values of $\pi d^3/32$ (d = diameter of shaft)

d	0	1/16	1/8	3/16	1/4	5/16	3/8	7/16	1/2	9/16	5/8	11/16	3/4	13/16	7/8	15/16	d
0	0	0.000024	0.00019	0.00065	0.00154	0.003	0.0052	0.0082	0.0123	0.0175	0.0239	0.0319	0.0414	0.0527	0.0658	0.0809	0
1	0.098	0.118	0.14	0.164	0.192	0.222	0.255	0.292	0.331	0.375	0.421	0.472	0.526	0.585	0.647	0.714	1
2	0.785	0.862	0.942	1.028	1.118	1.214	1.315	1.422	1.534	1.652	1.776	1.906	2.042	2.184	2.333	2.489	2
3	2.651	2.82	2.996	3.18	3.37	3.568	3.774	3.988	4.208	4.439	4.676	4.923	5.176	5.44	5.712	5.995	3
4	6.283	6.58	6.892	7.21	7.535	7.876	8.220	8.580	8.946	9.326	9.712	10.11	10.52	10.94	11.38	11.82	4
5	12.27	12.74	13.22	13.71	14.20	14.72	15.24	15.73	16.33	16.89	17.42	18.06	18.66	19.28	19.91	20.55	5
6	21.21	21.88	22.56	23.26	23.97	24.70	25.44	26.19	26.96	27.75	28.55	29.36	30.19	31.04	31.90	32.78	6
7	33.68		35.51		37.41		39.38		41.42		43.52		45.70		47.95		7
8	50.27		52.66		55.13		57.67		60.29		62.99		65.77		68.63		8
9	71.57		74.59		77.70		80.90		84.17		87.54		90.99		94.53		9
10	98.18		101.9		105.7		109.6		113.6		117.8		122.0		126.3		10
11	130.7		135.2		139.8		144.5		149.3		154.2		159.3		164.4		11
12	169.7		175.0		180.5		186.0		191.8		197.6		203.5		209.5		12
13	215.7		222.0		228.4		234.9		241.6		248.3		255.2		262.2		13
14	269.4		276.7		284.1		291.6		299.3		307.1		315.1		323.1		14
15	331.3		339.7		348.2		356.8		365.6		374.5		383.6		392.8		15

TABLE A.14
DECIMAL EQUIVALENTS OF FRACTIONS
(Advancing by Sixty-fourths)

$\frac{1}{64}$			= 0.015625	$\frac{33}{64}$			= 0.515625
	$\frac{1}{32}$		= 0.03125		$\frac{17}{32}$		= 0.53125
$\frac{3}{64}$			= 0.046875	$\frac{35}{64}$			= 0.546875
		$\frac{1}{16}$	= 0.0625			$\frac{9}{16}$	= 0.5625
$\frac{5}{64}$			= 0.078125	$\frac{37}{64}$			= 0.578125
	$\frac{3}{32}$		= 0.09375		$\frac{19}{32}$		= 0.59375
$\frac{7}{64}$			= 0.109375	$\frac{39}{64}$			= 0.609375
		$\frac{1}{8}$	= 0.125			$\frac{5}{8}$	= 0.625
$\frac{9}{64}$			= 0.140625	$\frac{41}{64}$			= 0.640625
	$\frac{5}{32}$		= 0.15625		$\frac{21}{32}$		= 0.65625
$\frac{11}{64}$			= 0.171875	$\frac{43}{64}$			= 0.671875
		$\frac{3}{16}$	= 0.1875			$\frac{11}{16}$	= 0.6875
$\frac{13}{64}$			= 0.203125	$\frac{45}{64}$			= 0.703125
	$\frac{7}{32}$		= 0.21875		$\frac{23}{32}$		= 0.71875
$\frac{15}{64}$			= 0.234375	$\frac{47}{64}$			= 0.734375
		$\frac{1}{4}$	= 0.25			$\frac{3}{4}$	= 0.75
$\frac{17}{64}$			= 0.265625	$\frac{49}{64}$			= 0.765625
	$\frac{9}{32}$		= 0.28125		$\frac{25}{32}$		= 0.78125
$\frac{19}{64}$			= 0.296875	$\frac{51}{64}$			= 0.796875
		$\frac{5}{16}$	= 0.3125			$\frac{13}{16}$	= 0.8125
$\frac{21}{64}$			= 0.328125	$\frac{53}{64}$			= 0.828125
	$\frac{11}{32}$		= 0.34375		$\frac{27}{32}$		= 0.84375
$\frac{23}{64}$			= 0.359375	$\frac{55}{64}$			= 0.859375
		$\frac{3}{8}$	= 0.375			$\frac{7}{8}$	= 0.875
$\frac{25}{64}$			= 0.390625	$\frac{57}{64}$			= 0.890625
	$\frac{13}{32}$		= 0.40625		$\frac{29}{32}$		= 0.90625
$\frac{27}{64}$			= 0.421875	$\frac{59}{64}$			= 0.921875
		$\frac{7}{16}$	= 0.4375			$\frac{15}{16}$	= 0.9375
$\frac{29}{64}$			= 0.453125	$\frac{61}{64}$			= 0.953125
	$\frac{15}{32}$		= 0.46875		$\frac{31}{32}$		= 0.96875
$\frac{31}{64}$			= 0.484375	$\frac{63}{64}$			= 0.984375
		$\frac{1}{2}$	= 0.50				

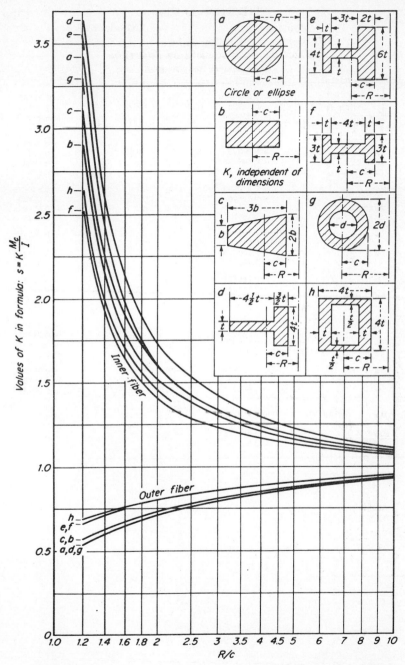

Fig. A.36. Factor K for beams of various cross sections. [After Wilson, B. J., and J. F. Quereau, "A Simple Method of Determining Stress in Curved Flexural Members," Circular No. 16, Engr. Exp. Station, Univ. of Illinois, January 1928.]

Section	Rectangular		Polar	
	Moment of Inertia I	$\dfrac{I}{C}$	Moment of Inertia J	$\dfrac{J}{r}$
	$\dfrac{bh^3}{12}$	$\dfrac{bh^2}{6}$		
	$\dfrac{\pi D^4}{64}$	$\dfrac{\pi D^3}{32}$	$\dfrac{\pi D^4}{32}$	$\dfrac{\pi D^3}{16}$
	$\dfrac{\pi(D^4 - d^4)}{64}$	$\dfrac{\pi(D^4 - d^4)}{32D}$	$\dfrac{\pi(D^4 - d^4)}{32}$	$\dfrac{\pi(D^4 - d^4)}{16D}$
	$\dfrac{D^4(9\pi^2 - 64)}{1152\pi}$			
	$\dfrac{\pi dD^3}{64}$			

INDEX